THE Doonbeg Ghosts

Old Tom Morris

Sir Alex Shaw

Dr Alister Mackenzie

Greg Norman

Bob Jones

Darren Clarke

The Author

James Carew

Pat Ruddy

THE
Doonbeg
Ghosts

IVAN MORRIS

Swing smooth & stay slán !

— Ivan Morris.

BECKENHAM

First published 2006 by Beckenham Publishing Limited,
Calamint House, PO Box 3339, Manchester M8 4XX, UK

Copyright © 2006 Ivan Morris
The moral right of Ivan Morris to be identified as author of this work
has been asserted by him in accordance with the Copyright, Designs and
Patents Act 1988.

A catalogue record for this book is available from the British Library.

ISBN 0-9548040-2-3
10 9 8 7 6 5 4 3 2 1
2010 2009 2008 2007 2006

Design: Robert Updegraff
Print production consultant: Geoff Barlow
Printed in Great Britain by MPG Books Limited, Bodmin

Photographs © Beckenham Publishing Limited 2006

look@pocket-golf.com   www.pocket-golf.com
www.photogolf.ie   www.photogolf.eu

This book is dedicated to the three brightest stars in my crown: my three children, Caroline, David and Sarah. Occasionally these shining stars have turned into thorns, but I love them with all of my heart and only wish that some day they would catch the golf bug as badly as I did.

The Author

Ivan Morris is a certified golf nut with the trophy to prove it. On the strength of his first book, *Only Golf Spoken Here*, published in 2001, he was voted Golf Nut of the Year by the Golf Nut Society of America – the first non-American to receive this dubious accolade. In a golf-saturated life, living, breathing and dreaming the game have resulted in extensive travels all over the globe in pursuit of the 'wee baw'. As well as attaining a coveted scratch handicap, Ivan has participated in countless Irish, British, European and American regional and national championships and has had many memorable personal encounters with some of the outstanding personalities in the game.

Ivan Morris is also the author of *The Life of O'Reilly,* a hilarious memoir of an infamous Irish professional caddie named Johnny O'Reilly (Sleeping Bear Press, 2002; softback Clock Tower Press, 2004, and John Wiley & Sons, 2005). Morris also contributed to Larry Lambrecht's handsome photographic coffee-table book on Irish seaside golf, *Emerald Gems* (2003), and is currently a senior columnist with Golf Digest *Ireland*, as well as being the principal contributing editor to the annual golfing almanac, *The Essential Golfer's Guide – Ireland.*

A long-standing and popular member of Limerick, Ballybunion and Lahinch Golf Clubs, Ivan Morris lives in Limerick, Ireland, with his long-suffering wife, Marie, and their three children (all of whom are golfers of varying enthusiasm and commitment).

Contents

Colour plates between pages 64 and 65

LIST OF ILLUSTRATIONS

Doonbeg 1st hole: an early-morning view.

Doonbeg 8th: the bunker-strewn approach to the green.

Doonbeg 12th: the green and its bunker from above.

Doonbeg 14th: the dramatic 111-yard hole.

Doonbeg 6th and 13th: an unusual crossover with Doughmore Beach beyond.

Lahinch (Old) 6th: the site of the new green.

Enniscrone 14th: the infamous dune, Cnoc na gCorp.

Royal County Down (Championship) 1st: beautiful but quirky.

Waterville 2nd: the typical Kerry surroundings.

The European 17th: Pat Ruddy's heavenly par 4.

All photographs by PhotoGolf

Frontispiece

For permission to reproduce photographs in the frontispiece, the author and publisher are grateful to Sidney L. Matthew of I. Q. Press, Pensacola, Florida, for the photograph of Bob Jones; Michael Galvin for the photograph of Darren Clarke; and Brian Stevens of Great White Shark Enterprises for the photograph of Greg Norman.

Acknowledgements

Writing, by its nature, is a solitary pursuit, but no book would ever see the light of day without the help of others. My wife, Marie, always gives me encouragement, co-operation and private space. It is hard to see how a single page could ever be filled without her.

As soon as I had formulated the roughest of outlines for this book, I showed it to my cousin Freddie Schwab at Strawberry Hill Golf Club in Middlesex and to my friend and chief literary critic Sten Mathews of Blainroe Golf Club in County Wicklow. Both of them said I just might be crazy enough to make the idea of playing golf with ghosts work.

James Carew's sisters, Lelia Hall and Trish Fitzgibbon, also read an early draft and kindly gave it their blessing, hopefully because they agreed with me that there are few better ways of immortalizing a loved one.

I am always grateful to my brothers, Brien and Dermot, who are excellent sounding-boards for my ideas. Brien also helps by allowing me the valuable use of scanning and photocopying facilities at McKerns Printing, Limerick.

I am most grateful to all the folks at Doonbeg, who have treated me as if I were royalty whenever I visit. To be truthful, I should not be all that flattered, because they treat every visitor similarly. When Doonbeg's head professional, Brian Shaw, saw an unedited copy, his enthusiasm put wind under my sails and the possibility of not reaching 'finality', as Alister Mackenzie would say, never arose again.

When I first wrote to Greg Norman seeking small points of clarification about his attitude to his Doonbeg project and golf architecture in general, I was not confident of ever receiving a reply. To my amazement we became pen pals! I hope I have captured his straightforward and committed approach in a manner that will please him and that he will enjoy reading about the few holes we 'played' together with Tom Churchill in tow. It was fun allowing my imagination a free rein during that episode!

When I bumped into Peter Millhouse and William fforde at Quinta de Cima in the Algarve, they were promoting their excellent *Pocket Guide to Golf Courses: Spain & Portugal.* They told me they were planning 'to do Ireland' next. I offered to help them, if I could, and a mutually enlightening and pleasant friendship began, further enriched when they visited me at home with their colleague Greg Turner. None of us could have anticipated that their company would end up publishing my next book. That happy outcome did not become part of the agenda until 'well into the back nine'.

This is my third book, so I thought I knew what to expect from publishers. My previous experience was to submit a draft, receive a contract offer, get paid and after that the writer had virtually no further input. The small publisher ethos at Beckenham makes it much more like a family affair: everybody is more involved with each other. Dealing with Brenda and Robert Updegraff, who edited and designed this book, was a joy. While Operations Manager Arnie Cohen is a paragon of quiet efficiency, Editor William fforde is like myself in that he tends to call a spade a shovel and does not suffer fools gladly. We may not always have seen eye to eye about everything right away, but in each case a happy resolution, and an improvement, were quickly found. I am most grateful to all of them!

Ivan Morris
Limerick, June 2006

Introduction

My parents, Tom and Bernie Morris, began playing golf in 1957. Within a short time they had turned the game into a way of life in our household and had infected their four sons with a bug that has remained stubbornly incurable in succeeding generations.

As the eldest, I became a golfing trail-blazer in my own right and ever since have been the leader of a pack of acknowledged golf nuts who have always striven to remain competitive with each other and with the rest of the world.

In my first year of golf, I met the Reverend Gerard Canon Enright, a parish priest affectionately known as Cannonball. The pun was intentional because he was such a proud big-hitter. Canon Enright introduced me to his own idea of heaven: Ballybunion Golf Club. He told me that if I could match par at 'Ballybee' I could do it anywhere. Despite the gap in our ages, we became such firm golf buddies that we regularly played forty-five holes in a day and went to Augusta together in 1981 to see what that reputed 'heaven' was all about. Cannonball gave me my first golf book, *Down the Fairway* by Bobby Jones. That book helped to give me a respect and understanding of the game that has continued to grow with the passing years.

A year or two before he departed this vale of tears, Cannonball lost his sight, but not his love of golf. I used to visit him regularly to give him the most detailed of blow-by-blow accounts of my rounds and analytical descriptions of any new golf courses or golfers, especially big-hitters, that I had seen.

Not long before he died, Cannonball volunteered that he would somehow get a report back to me on the quality of golf in heaven after he had passed on. But he did not keep his promise. Instead, it was left to another lifelong golf companion of mine to inform me about golf in the after-life. My late friend James Carew did visit me in one of my golf dreams and told me, in the matter-of-fact tone that was so typical of him, that golf in heaven was exactly the same as it is on Earth – paradoxical and frustrating. Frustration may not be everyone's idea of heaven, but if golf is involved I want to be a part of it for all eternity. I love the game that much.

When I wrote my first book, *Only Golf Spoken Here*, I had only the vaguest idea of what I was trying to achieve. My second effort, *The Life of O'Reilly*, was somewhat similar. After this book, my third, I have come to the realization that that is the way of books. Once words are put on a page they tend to take up a life of their own, leading both writer and reader into unimaginable places. So it has been with *The Doonbeg Ghosts*, which has grown out of an enthusiastic email I wrote to friends after I had played Doonbeg for the first time with Ed Tovey and Derry Culligan, my equals as committed and devoted golfers I hasten to add.

To call me an avid reader of golf books would be a grave understatement. For as long as I can remember, my quest for golfing knowledge has been insatiable, whether it be the facts and figures of tournament results, anecdotes, technique, psychology, the game's history or course architecture. All have been passions surpassed only by my quest to keep my handicap as close to scratch as possible.

Many of the quotations in *The Doonbeg Ghosts* are products of my imagination based on what I have read over the years about the views and opinions of the characters involved. A few have been taken directly from books in my cherished library and 'tweaked' to suit whatever message I was trying to transmit at the time. I would warmly recommend readers to try the books listed below. Maybe then they will realize that this book is not quite as far-fetched as they first thought?

Barkow, Al, and Sarazen, Mary-Ann, *Gene Sarazen and Shell's Wonderful World of Golf* (Clock Tower Press, 2003).

Byrdy, Stan, *The Augusta National Golf Club – Dr Alister Mackenzie's Masterpiece* (Media Sports Group, 2005).

Doak, Tom, Scott, Dr James S., and Haddock, Raymund M., *The Life and Work of Dr Alister Mackenzie* (Sleeping Bear Press, 2001).

Faldo, Nick, *Life Swings – The Autobiography* (Headline, 2004).

Haultain, Arnold, *The Mystery of Golf* (first published in 1908; reprinted by Sleeping Bear Press, 2001).

Jones, Bobby, *Down the Fairway* (Chatto and Windus, 1961).

Joy, David, *The Scrapbook of Old Tom Morris* (Sleeping Bear Press, 2001).

Mackenzie, Dr Alister, *The Spirit of St Andrews* (Sleeping Bear Press, 1999).

Matthew, Sidney L., *The Wit and Wisdom of Bobby Jones* (Clock Tower Press, 2003).

Matthew, Sidney L., *Bobby Jones Extra!* (Sports Media Group, 2004).

Matthew, Sidney L., *The Life and Times of Bobby Jones* (Sports Media Group, 2005).

Shackleford, Geoff, *The Future of Golf* (Sasquash Books, 2004).

Shedloski, David S., *Golden Twilight* (Sleeping Bear Press, 2001).

James (aka Tail Gunner) Carew

(1946–1998)

FROM 1954 TO 1964, James Carew and I were classmates at the sports-mad Jesuit-run Crescent College in Limerick. Apart from our classical education, we played tennis, soccer, hockey and rugby together, some of them up to under-age international standard: James in tennis and hockey, me in soccer and rugby. However, when we discovered golf it almost immediately took over as our primary sporting passion. For nearly forty years we travelled to the four corners of Ireland, and further afield, in pursuit of golfing adventures and excellence. As we grew older, the philosophy of golf and its architecture, rather than swing techniques and how to win tournaments, became our main talking points. We were such close friends throughout all of that time that James's untimely death in 1998 at the age of fifty-one has meant that I miss him like a lost brother.

I often wonder how James would react to the fact that somebody he jokingly referred to as 'the Nut' long before I ever became a member of 'the committed' and 'an officially and fully-certified golf nut', had found the courage – or, maybe, the confounded cheek – to write about the game. Well, the truth is, if James was still on this Earth I would probably be content just to be talking about golf with him instead of writing about it.

Anyone who ever travelled to a sporting event of any kind with James Carew will vouch for his sharp skills of observation and his tactical savvy. Before and after matches, no matter what the code, collective and individual performances were parsed in minute detail. James knew all about the psychology of sport, especially team sports, long before most of us ever heard of mental gurus.

Forthright but diplomatic, James had strong opinions on many subjects, but he also possessed the admirable gift of remaining cool and making his point without becoming emotional. His ability to get to the heart of any matter quickly would have made him a successful politician like his father, the late John Carew, a former Mayor of Limerick, but James did not choose that path.

James was no shrinking violet: he could cut you up in pieces with a verbal barrage if he thought you deserved it. In our home town of Limerick, he was a mentor and inspiration to many aspiring sportsmen and sportswomen. The wise ones sought his advice often, and he never failed to give an honest opinion straight from the heart and to the point. Many have good reason to remember his generosity of spirit. A scrupulously fair opponent, James had a countrywide reputation as a steely competitor. He may not have been flamboyant, but he made his presence felt everywhere he went.

James is sadly missed by his family and by fellow-members at his beloved Ballyclough (Limerick Golf Club), where he was an indispensible, stalwart member of five All-Ireland-winning Senior and Junior Cup campaigns.

Ivan Morris

1

The Opera Singer

W ITHOUT SO MUCH as a glance behind us, despite the
excitement we had experienced only a few moments
earlier, Tail Gunner and I marched briskly down the
steep slope at the back of the 11th green at Doonbeg Golf Club in
westernmost Ireland. As we made our way around the corner of
the shaggy dune on top of which the 12th tee (401 yards, par 4) is
perched, we were startled to overhear Papageno's opening aria
from Mozart's *The Magic Flute* being sung in beautiful German.

'What in heaven's name is that?' exclaimed my companion,
James (aka Tail Gunner) Carew. (The Tail Gunner reference
relates to James's normal position of being 'last man' on Limerick
Golf Club teams. His unflappability and ability to raise his game
in a crisis was frequently called upon and never found wanting,
as five All-Ireland winning medals attest.)

Within moments, we discovered that the voice belonged to a
handsome, stocky gentleman of about thirty years of age, wearing
a fetching straw hat. Neatly dressed in dated but impeccable golfing attire, the singer had a deep tan, dark brown hair and a winning smile. He wore stone-grey plus-fours that emphasized his
powerful, tree-trunk thighs; sky-blue knee-socks; a long-sleeved,
dazzlingly white silk shirt with a saffron Augusta National Golf
Club tie; USGA-engraved gold cufflinks and matching tie-pin; a
cotton sports jacket that matched the colour of the socks perfectly;
and brown-and-white golf shoes that sparkled in the early evening

sunlight. Elegantly brandishing a lighted cigarette in an ebony holder in his right hand (presumably to conduct an imaginary orchestra), he had a highly polished, hickory-shafted blunderbuss of a wooden-headed driver tucked neatly under his left arm. Charisma and self-assurance exuded from his every pore.

'Sure is nice to meet y'all. My name is Robert Tyre Jones Junior. May I tag along with you fellows for a few holes of gentle flog?'

Even though the smile was friendly and sincere, I was dumb-founded. Tongue-tied, I looked at my companion, hoping that he would possess the composure to respond. After all, Tail Gunner was a ghost too. He had joined me earlier in my round, at the 7th hole, to fulfil a long-established promise we had made to inform each other about the quality of golf in the after-life. He should have been accustomed to meeting famous deceased golfers.

For almost forty years, ever since we were kids in school together, the late James 'Tail Gunner' Carew was my friend, soul mate and most frequent golf companion. As young lads we played rugby, soccer, tennis and hockey together. In our mid-teens, our respective fathers, both long-serving members and captains of Limerick Golf Club, introduced us to the fascinations of golf. From that moment onwards we spent the lion's share of our recreation time travelling around Ireland, Britain and Europe playing in golf tournaments of varying importance.

We were planning to continue our golfing odysseys together as senior golfers when, out of the blue, at the age of only fifty-one, Tail Gunner discovered he had a genetic heart problem that required surgery. To the distress of everybody who knew him, James did not make it through – he passed away unexpectedly on the operating table, illustrating the stark reality of how fragile the grip on life can be even for the strongest and fittest amongst us.

On our various travels Tail Gunner and I often joked that if there was no golf in heaven neither of us would be all that inter-ested in going there. A few weeks after he had passed on, Tail Gunner did, I am convinced, honour our pact of sending back a message to confim the quality, or otherwise, of golf in the after-life when he appeared in one of my dreams and reassured me that, 'Nothing to worry about! Golf in heaven is exactly the same as it is on Earth: paradoxical, unpredictable and endlessly fascinating. You will love it!'

Then the ghost had disappeared without giving me an appointment for my first tee-time. I never again heard from Tail Gunner until the unforgettable day that I am about to describe.

'Delighted to meet you, Mr Jones. As you are a newcomer to this part of the world, we will gladly concede the honour. Please play away,' he said, with the minimum of fuss, before turning to me and whispering, 'I knew that this was on the cards. I heard Jones was doing a tour of the great Irish courses and felt sure that if I hung around here at Doonbeg the opportunity to meet him would present itself sooner or later. You hardly believe that I came all the way from eternity just to golf with you?'

'Say y'all, if you don't mind, please call me Bob, not Bobby, and pardon me for saying so but your narrow Irish roads would scare the hell out of a body, if it were mortal that is, but I sure enjoyed the experience of travelling by automobile in real time along that scenic coast road between Lahinch and Doonbeg. Earlier today I had the pleasure of playing a game with John Burke. What a stylish exponent! As for that Lahinch layout, it is one of the best tracks I ever set foot on. If a fellow can beat old man par there he can darn well do it anywhere,' drawled Jones. He treated us as if we were long-lost buddies of his, while at the same time he blew enormous clouds of disconcerting cigarette smoke in all directions.

Getting over my initial shock, I tentatively joined in the conversation, finding the wit to say, 'That Burke fellow could play all right. He wasn't called the King of Lahinch for nothing. From the late 1920s to the mid-1940s he was virtually unbeatable over his home course. I'm not sure if you realize that you two narrowly missed opposing each other in the Walker Cup? When John played at Brookline in 1932 it was one series too late, because you had quit in 1930. John should have been selected in 1928, but the selectors were a biased group who did not think an Irish Republican should be eligible to play for Great Britain and they overlooked his outstanding credentials. By 1932, the political climate had changed sufficiently to allow Burke to be included. During his long career, Burke won the Irish National Amateur eight times and the South of Ireland Amateur Championship eleven times.'

'Yes sir! Burke told me all about Brookline, giving me one of those dreaded blow-by-blows of his singles match with Jack Westland. Darn it, the match went the full thirty-six holes before ending up all square.' Jones chuckled heartily.

'To tell you the truth,' he went on, a little sadly now, 'I was more interested in finding out about John's parallel life experience to mine: ending up in a wheelchair while still a relatively young man. Like me, he was prevented from being able to play social golf with his buddies into venerable old age, which I am sure he would have enjoyed.'

'Why do you continue to play golf in the after-life, Bob?' asked Tail Gunner. 'Do you still find the challenges of the game fascinating?'

Jones seemed to have a well-prepared answer to that potentially complex question.

'To the uninitiated, golf appears to be a dignified, mannerly game played with decorum and not too much fire in the belly. How wrong they are! Golf is an athletic pursuit of considerable passion. It's a game that burns inwardly, searing the soul. It can be quite explosive, as I demonstrated far too often by losing my temper when least expected. Long after I had ceased to play the game seriously, I remained utterly devoted to it and entranced by it.'

Bob Jones may or may not have realized it, but by answering that question in such a thought-provoking way he had invited big trouble. A touch more aggressively than intended, I blurted out something that had been sitting uneasily on my mind since I had first heard it.

'If you were that entranced by the game, why did you retire so young? Ken Venturi told me when I met him at Lahinch last year that Gene Sarazen had always maintained that you quit because you were unable to make a successful transition from hickory to steel shafts.'

'That little Italian was always talking hogwash, always applying the needle. He used to stick his needles in me at every opportunity when we played. Apparently he has not lost the habit. Sarazen hated to be beaten by me because I was an amateur. He felt it reflected badly on his profession. With that outsize ego of his, Sarazen should have been a screen actor. Wait a minute! As the host of *Shell's Wonderful World of Golf* for nine years, he was one! That television series gave many people, including me, a lot of pleasure. The way Gene could turn on and off the charm was really something. During his career, he pretended to be friendly and cheerful all the time, but you better believe that he was ruthless when the chance to win a golf tournament arose. Sarazen may have been the toughest competitor I ever came across.'

Far from being irritated by our questions, Bob Jones was really warming up now and in full flow.

'As for Venturi's comments about steel shafts, I would like to point out, because it is not widely known, that when I went over to playing steel for the first time in 1932 – to help promote my own signature clubs, which I helped to design for the Spalding Company (the first matched set of clubs ever made, by the way) – I broke seventy in the first seven rounds I played with them. Then when I played in the inaugural Augusta Invitational (Masters) Tournament in 1934 – as a ceremonial golfer in my own tournament rather than as a serious competitor, because when I retired from competition in 1930 I never had any intention of making the necessary effort or sacrifices to try to win again – my play from tee to green with those steel shafts was as good as it ever was at any time during my career. Unfortunately, my touch with Calamity Jane, my beloved putter, deserted me. To be honest, the fire in my belly for competition had gone out and my nerves were finally shot. I was burned out and could no longer focus on getting the ball into the hole with the intensity that is needed to win. For the first time in my life, I did not care what score I shot. The hunger and drive just weren't there any more. I had begun to treat golf as a distraction. I was content to be out of the office and playing social golf with my friends. Dipping in and out of competition does not work because the mental side gets flabby if not exercised continually. I had had enough of golf stress, I guess.' Jones shook his head.

'Is that why you gave up?' enquired Tail Gunner softly.

'No. I gave up championship play because my wife, Mary, to whom I was devoted, told me it was high time to start giving my family responsibilities and legal career my full energy and attention. Disappearing for months on end during the summer was unfair on her bringing up a family of three children. To be honest with you, giving up travelling all around the United States playing for trinkets and glory was no hardship. I was tired of it. Tired of the crowds and the adulation; never felt one bit comfortable with that.

'At the end of the 1928 season, Mary stepped up her campaign to rein me in. She decreed that the time was coming to put golf to one side. I had been gadding about the country as an amateur golfer for fifteen years. Amateur golf would not pay any of the bills. Soon after I got my head around the undeniable fact that there were more important things in life than winning golf tournaments, I decided that I would quit at the first ideal opportunity.'

'Why is golf such a difficult game?' I asked.

'Too much down-time, too much time to think between shots. It may be why some people say that golf is a good walk spoiled,' came the instant reply.

'But that's the very nature of the game!' Tail Gunner declared and then, showing his eagerness for education from one of the game's greatest heroes, he asked, 'How can you overcome it?'

'In golf, probably less than one per cent of the time on the course is spent actually hitting the ball. That means you have to control your mental activity for ninety-nine per cent of the time to remain fully focused. Golf does not allow one to run off one's tensions; everything happens so slowly and the act of striking the ball is over in a flash. That's the supreme mental challenge. It took me for ever to learn how to cope. My mind was constantly wandering off the job. Especially if things were going really well, I could become stupidly careless and lose the train of what I should be doing. I never really mastered this failing. The mental toughness of players like Sarazen, Nelson, Hogan, Nicklaus and, now, Tiger Woods is what separates them.'

'Was mental toughness part of your nature or did you have to practise it to perfect it?' I asked.

'Not part of my nature at all. Mental toughness is an acquired skill; anyone can learn it if they are fully dedicated to the task. Anybody can do it if they want to badly enough.' While that statement may have sounded plausible, personally I was not convinced, but I didn't want to be argumentative; I decided to change the subject and maybe try to broach it again later.

'Did John Burke say anything to you about the changes that have taken place at Lahinch since his era? I can well imagine the reintroduction of all those wild, Mackenzie-like undulations on the greens giving him fits.'

'You've got that right!' Jones exclaimed. 'Burke said he sure would love to put a bulldozer to some of those Mackenzie undulations, which, amazingly, he told me is exactly what he did do back in 1941 when he was Captain of the Club. Above all though, Burke seemed perplexed by the destruction of the former 3rd hole, a par 3, right beside the clubhouse. He told me that it was a tiny, postage-stamp affair that required an extremely precise mashie stroke, especially in a crosswind. He also said that he was surprised that the Klondike sandhill that dominates the 4th hole had not been bombed out of existence. Apparently it has always been a dangerous crossover point, and with so many people playing the game in the litigious twenty-first century, it is more dangerous than ever. As for the quirky, blind par 3 Dell [the 5th],

John said that he never liked that particular hole, but because Old Tom Morris built it in 1894 it was ingrained into the traditions of Lahinch and would be there for ever.

'Burke also told me a cute story about the day he defeated my Irish buddy Joe Carr in the "South Final" of '46. I got to know Joe quite well when he played in the Masters Tournament as British Amateur Champ on a number of occasions. Those who saw that Burke–Carr match claim that it was the greatest head-to-head match of all time. After a titanic battle littered with birdies and eagles, Carr overcame a considerable early deficit to be one up coming down the last hole. The youngster hit an enormous drive down the centre of the 36th fairway, 30 yards or so ahead of his rapidly tiring opponent. With mischief written all over his face, Burke told me that he put one of his infamous decoy routines into play. In advance, he had worked out a scheme with his caddie to help him outsmart opponents. The scam was that if he called out loud twice for any club, in this case his spoon [3-wood], the caddie should not move a muscle but allow his master to dip into the bag and make his own selection. In this case, John pulled the driver instead. Letting fly as hard as he could, he nipped the ball as sweet as a nut straight off the deck. The ball pitched on the back of a friendly mound and scooted forward into the middle of the raised green, 270 yards away. Carr fell for the ruse. He selected a 2-iron, which came up well short of the target. Burke won the hole and went on to defeat Carr at the now "disappeared" third extra hole. A wonderful story!'

Then the operatic singing resumed in a low, rhythmical hum; lazy waggles grew longer and more vigorous. A pronounced forward press followed as those tanned, powerful hands took the club into a long, slow back swing that travelled well past parallel. Jones appeared to be made of rubber as he turned his left shoulder under his chin. There was a sudden and distinct shift of body position as his left heel was stamped firmly on the ground before the club was pulled down in a blur of speed, meeting the cream-coloured Spalding Dot with a loud, distinctive click. The ball seemed to adhere to the club face momentarily before soaring away, gaining height for nine-tenths of its journey before suddenly losing momentum and dropping straight down to earth behind a low ditch, approximately twenty paces to the right of where I thought the centre of the fairway was.

'Is that the correct line?' I asked, slightly alarmed.

'If you can carry the ball 240 yards or better, that is perfect. It's a short cut that sets up the best approach to a most unusual green,' said Jones, a trifle enigmatically.

As I teed up my ball, I noticed my hands were shaking. I tried to calm my nerves by taking a few deep breaths. I shook my arms and stretched out my fingers. My driver felt strange and heavier than normal, and I peered anxiously down at it. I could not believe my eyes when I saw the first brand-new driver that I had ever purchased from my own resources, in 1961, a beautiful pear-shaped, laminated, wood, painted bright red with the words 'Spalding – Robt. T. Jones Jnr.' printed on it in a flowing white script. In my sweating palms, the long-discarded club felt as if it weighed about 10 kilos. The extra weight seemed to slow down my swing. For once I maintained my posture and spine angle, and I pounded a terrific shot on the same line and trajectory as Jones. My ball barely cleared the ditch – but enough is enough, and it took a few sprightly hops forward before stumbling to a halt 5 yards short of where Jones's ball had come to rest.

Tail Gunner was never able to fly the ball high or achieve much in the way of hang-time. With his feet (legitimately) outside the designated teeing area, he placed his ball tight to the marker on the left-hand side of the tee box before hitting one of his trademark low skimmers. The ball ran and skipped along the left-hand side of the fairway, close to an out-of-bounds fence, before eventually stopping a long way behind Jones and me. For his second effort, Tail Gunner played another daisy-cutter, this time with his 4-wood. The ball found the front left corner of the green. Ignoring the flag, I played into the middle of the green, where my ball took one vigorous hop forward before disappearing.

At this stage, Tail Gunner and I were blissfully unaware of what our next tasks were going to be. Hidden from view, a small sand bunker is quixotically located in the middle of the green. We were soon to discover that the trap had stymied Tail Gunner's route to the hole, whereas my ball rested snugly in the middle of the sand. Caressing his ball with a deft flick of a silver-bladed niblick, Bob played towards the back right-hand corner of the green; the ball ran up a slope before turning around and trickling slowly backwards towards the centre of the green.

Accepting the disappointing result with enviable calmness, Tail Gunner played first, putting past the trap to the back edge of the green. From there, he would be able to make a more conventional approach towards the hole in due course. Determined to emulate Tail Gunner's example of restraint, I rid myself of the annoyance I felt by digging my feet more deeply than I usually would into the soft sand and feathered a delicate recovery to within 4 feet of the target.

Now it was Bob's turn. He waved his famous Calamity Jane putter over the ball as if blessing it. Then he placed the putter head down in front of the ball before lifting it back over it again. One final, quick look at the hole and he sent the ball on its way down the slope with the gentlest of taps that disguised a distinct, accelerating hit. With its very last gasp the ball reached the hole and toppled in.

'Birdie!' we all shouted in unison.

It was now Tail Gunner's turn to putt, but he came up 9 inches short, bogey 5. Ignoring whatever subtle breaks may have been present on my line to the hole, I willed my 4-footer into the cup for a scrambling par. My match with the Doonbeg Ghost was back to where it had started, all square.

2

The Wages of Sin

W E WERE NOW PLAYING right down the spine of the golf course. Measuring 500 yards bang on the nose, the 13th fairway is a roller-coaster of uninterrupted turbulence. Just past halfway, the hole veers to the right and goes sharply uphill. Sixty yards short of the green, a mountainous barrier of unruly scrub and savage bunkers has to be surmounted. At this point, bail-outs or alternative routes become non-existent. You have no choice but to overcome those obstacles or fail to complete the hole.

Aiming directly over a white marker stone lying forlornly in the centre of a narrow pathway, Jones hammered another powerful drive in the direction of the hidden fairway. Attempting to follow suit, my connection was less than perfect and the ball drifted 20 yards to the right of where I had intended. As always, Tail Gunner's Penfold flew low, hard and straight as a die, barely skimming over the white marker stone before racing forwards into a deep hollow among the fairway waves. Three abreast, we strode purposefully forward.

When we halted to view the magnificent golfing valley ahead of us, Tail Gunner promised our guest that he would 'shut up' and allow him to enjoy his game in peace. The gesture was declined with the elaborate wave of an orchestra conductor's hand. He said he was not remotely interested in 'dour Hoganesque golf' and instead began to drive the conversation.

No matter what Tail Gunner and I threw at him thereafter, Jones remained unruffled. His relaxed air and garrulous, throaty chuckle were a delight as he engaged us with good-humoured honesty and down-to-earth frankness.

'What was the singing about, Bob?' I asked.

'My mother, Clara, loved the opera, especially German opera, and my father, the Colonel, was an accomplished baritone. For as long as I can remember our home was filled with music from sunrise to dusk. From my earliest beginnings in golf, my warm-up routines have always been accompanied by an aria to help me get my tempo into smooth running order.'

Then, as if anticipating our next series of questions, Jones continued, 'From an early stage I was subconsciously aware that there might be a kind of golfing destiny planned for me – although, obviously, I was not fully certain what exactly it might be. Buried in the back of my mind was the notion that I had been given the gift to set golfing records. After I won the National Opens double in 1926, I thought that that might have been it and I even considered quitting there and then, but I must have been greedy and thought that if I could win the US Amateur at Pebble Beach in 1929 for an unprecedented third time in a row, then I would finally stop. From 1926 on, I was on the lookout for the right moment to end and almost did on a few occasions. The US Amateur hat-trick would have been the perfect signing-off note, I thought. But if I had retired at that time the so-called 'Jones Mystique', which the writers O. B. Keeler and Grantland Rice had carefully created, would surely have faded away.

'A youngster named Johnny Goodman rode down to California from Omaha, Nebraska, in a boxcar and done bushwhacked all of my plans. Goodman caused a huge shock and rethink by dumping me squarely on my backside. All thoughts of retirement had to be banished for one more year. I did not enjoy the experience of travelling the width of America to lose in the first round of match play to an unknown, but I fully understood that these things happen in golf.

'In the run-up to that first-ever USGA Championship west of the Mississippi, my position had been somewhat complicated by the fact that I was aware that the USGA were considering changing the rules of amateur status. Although I never earned any cash directly from playing the game, it is true that I had been in receipt of gifts for many years that under the proposed new rules could not have been entertained. Secretly, I had been offered a quarter of a million dollar Hollywood movie deal. In order to accept the fortune, I knew that I would have to quit and become a "non-amateur". It would have taken me a lifetime to amass that much liquid cash. In 1929, professional golfers barely eked out a living and were not highly regarded socially. I was well aware that if I had gone into the paid ranks with the sole purpose of cashing in, the mystical aura that was to be my legacy would have been destroyed. At no stage did I consider professional golf as an option. My contemporaries Francis Ouimet and Chick Evans did not rush into the paid ranks either. We agreed amongst ourselves that we would have hated the lifestyle of being a travelling circus act playing golf for relative peanuts.'

'Did your wife accompany you on many of your trips?' I asked.

'Although she did go with me on that unforgettable cross-country train trip to California in 1929, Mary was a home bird. She was highly strung and hated fuss. Although I liked her to be with me, she always succeeded in making me more damn nervous than I would have been without her. After the débâcle in California, with the help of the Colonel and my constant travelling companion 'Pop' Keeler, I managed to persuade Mary to allow me one more summer of travel so that I could finish my career on a suitable high note. She agreed, provided she could travel to Britain with me and that a shopping trip to Paris would be included in our itinerary. Up until then, winning the British Amateur had eluded me, but it was important for my place in history and for boosting the movies I knew I was going to make that I fill that void. After what happened in 1930, retiring became the easiest decision I ever had to make. As soon as I ceased playing competitively my nerve and desire quickly left me and I never got it back. Once there was nothing left to prove, the incentive was gone. From then on, any public golf that I played was purely ceremonial to help a good cause. The last time I played in a serious competition was the "unofficial" US National Open of 1942 in Chicago, won by Ben Hogan. Although it was a few years yet before I ended up in that damn wheelchair, I had so many aches in my legs, neck and shoulders after playing at Chicago that I suspected I was all washed up.'

Feeling that Jones was enjoying his reminiscing, Tail Gunner plucked up the courage to ask, 'What was your most memorable moment?'

'Probably what happened after winning the big Open double on both sides of the Atlantic in 1926. We had a fairly uneventful trip home from England on the *Aquatania* and were approaching the Verrazano Bridge on entering New York Harbor when Keeler asked me to join him up on deck. There, I was stunned to find that several dozen friends and family, including Mary and my grandaddy Big Bob, who barely tolerated my golf career, had travelled from Atlanta and had come out on the Narrows by tugboat to greet us. Ships' sirens began sounding off all around us, creating the most dreadful din. Soon after we docked, there was a ticker-tape parade through the streets of New York. I couldn't understand why an amateur golfer from the South would be treated in this way. Sometime later Walter Hagen told me, with a hint of jealousy, that Grantland Rice and the USGA were behind it, aided and abetted by the Mayor of New York, Jimmy Walker, who, like many politicians, was a self-publicist with a fetish for being photographed with celebrities. It appeared to me as if the entire population of New York had gone mad. Keeler wrote later, "Ticker tape [was] flying in white spirals from the skyscrapers and a continuous roar echoed through the canyons of downtown New York." I couldn't believe that people who would not know one end of a spade mashie from the other were honouring me in this way. All I wanted to do was have a few quiet moments with Mary and go home to Atlanta, but it was impossible.'

When I asked the next question, Tail Gunner's eyes did cart-wheels and he took a sharp intake of breath. 'From your point of view, tell me about that $50,000 gift that the City of Atlanta gave you. It seems to have caused trouble between you and the USGA.'

'I'll be glad to set the record straight,' replied Jones. 'Many of my fellow-Atlantans were still feeling bruised after the Civil War and needed to have their feelings of self-worth reinforced. The city fathers maintained that I was the South's finest ambassador and promoter. They loved putting on a parade whenever I won a national championship. At one of those interminable dinners in my honour, out of the blue the Mayor presented me with a cheque for $50,000 to help Mary and me build a home in our native city. The money had been raised by small donations from members of the Atlanta Athletic Club. There was nothing written in the rules about the rights and wrongs of keeping the money, and the USGA never actually told me that I should give it back, but they did make their disapproval plain. I admit that I was tempted. I kept the uncashed cheque in a safe in my office for two months before eventually turning it back. Relying entirely on my salary from Jones, Evins, Moore & Jones, Attorneys at Law, Mary and I got our own house in the spring of 1928. It was a more modest home than we could have had with the $50,000, but we were happy in it. We did not want a cloud over us for the rest of our lives. We both knew the promised film contract in the pipeline would take care of everything soon enough. It was the first time in my life that my grandfather seemed pleased with me. He told me he was glad I was prepared to stand on my own two feet and not rely on gifts to make my way in the world. Grandaddy always considered golf to be a waste of time.

'Apart from my career in the practice of law, I loved writing my own golf column, which was syndicated to newspapers nationwide. That was within amateur rules and it paid quite well. Writing technical advice for so-called hackers became a distinct advantage when I had to articulate my swing thoughts making those films for Warner Brothers.'

Jones gave a sudden snort of belly laughter. 'Chick Evans tried to have me banned, you know,' he said. 'He told the USGA that I was a sham amateur. I would not like to repeat what I told him about that accusation. I was a lawyer. I knew I was not breaking any rules. I guess Chick and I had been rubbing each other up the wrong way for years.'

Tail Gunner was visibly shocked by this revelation. 'I'm astonished to hear you say that about Chick Evans. Tell us more.'

'Sure, Chick was a terrific ball-striker. Unfortunately for him, his putting let him down, especially whenever he went head-to-head against me. I guess he tried too hard. Although Chick and I did not like each other personally, all of our public matches were played in the proper spirit. Chick was an ex-caddie out of Chicago and was jealous that he was not born with the privileges that I enjoyed. Why he should blame me for an accident of birth baffled me. I never looked up or down my nose at anybody and accepted all-comers on their merits. Chick and I made our US Open débuts in 1914 and he nearly won, finishing only one stroke behind Walter Hagen. Our rivalry began. I had travelled from Atlanta with Keeler and we were the houseguests of his friend Grantland Rice, the sports writer. Rice made a huge fuss over me and ignored Evans. It was unfair and overdone, but it was not of my doing. From that moment, Chick got it into his head to run against me. It became a kind of obsession. With hindsight, we should have grown out of it a lot sooner than we did. Chick did beat me hollow in one area: his tournament career lasted until well into his seventies, whereas I was done before I hit thirty.'

'Could you identify the greatest golf shot you ever played?' I asked.

'A typical golf nut question!' exclaimed Tail Gunner.

'Well now, to be honest I remember the pain caused by my mis-cues far more clearly. I could fill a book talking about them. Never forget that I had seven lean years before I finally felt the relief of coming out on top. Some of the mistakes I made in that period still haunt me, but without doubt my most important single shot had to be the driving-iron approach to the green of the final play-off hole with Bobby Cruickshank at Inwood in 1923. It secured my first win in the US Open. I felt it in my bones that it was a now-or-never moment. Not thinking about the risks involved, I decided to rely on instinct and play quickly while my anxious followers' hearts were in their mouths. Happily, the shot came off perfectly. Perhaps it was the fickle finger of fate deciding that my time had come, because I was completely exhausted and could not have walked another yard. I had to finish the match with one swing or I was a goner.'

'Why did you build Augusta National?' Tail Gunner asked.

'To give something back to the game that had been so wonderful to me. Dr Alister Mackenzie and Clifford Roberts (an Iowan who became a successful New York investment banker and ran Augusta National Golf Club as its chairman in legendary, innovative but despotic fashion from its foundation until his death in 1977) helped me to succeed beyond my wildest dreams. I am certain that Augusta and what it means to the game has done more to elevate my standing in golf history than my championship wins. The continuing popularity of the Masters Tournament is very gratifying. We were blessed that the gorgeous Berckman's nursery land was available.

'I met Mac at the Walker Cup matches in St Andrews in 1926. We conversed at great length and realized we had similar philosophies. When I saw what he had created at Cypress Point in California, I knew that he was the one to design my golf course. Mac conceived the routing during a three-day visit in April 1932. He did make one more trip, in October of the same year, before the seeding was complete, but he never saw the course again. He was supposed to come again in June 1933 but sent his associate Marion Hollins instead. Sadly, it was a deliberate snub because Cliff, who controlled the purse strings, was in default over the payment of overdue fees. We almost went bankrupt in 1933. The whole country was in financial turmoil trying to recover from the

1929 Wall Street Crash. Finding investors at that time was not easy. We were desperately short of cash. Sadly, Mac died in January 1934, two and a half months before the official opening, and the matter was never resolved.

'The Crash had a huge impact on Mackenzie and the subsequent money worries put an intolerable strain on him. Before 1929 business was booming and he was building courses all over the world. When all investment in golf, or anything else for that matter, ground to a halt, Mac never got over the shock. He had been living beyond his means and all of a sudden he could not collect what he was owed.

'Mac was a wonder. After seeing the property for the first time, he stayed up all night and managed to draw up the entire routing in one sitting. I sat with him and together we polished off three bottles of Old Rarity. The second and third days were spent fine-tuning and checking distances by hitting golf balls. I had a severe headache in the strong sunshine, but Mac breezed through it all nonchalantly. Later, Cliff Roberts was responsible for making an inspired change to Mackenzie's original plan: he reversed the nines.'

'What do you think of the addition of rough at Augusta in recent years and, in general, the way the USGA sets up its courses in the twenty-first century?' Tail Gunner seemed to be surprised by my line of questioning, but Jones was unfazed.

'I didn't always see eye to eye with the blazers of the USGA. They have always believed in the Calvinistic philosophy that "golf sins" should not be forgiven and any hope of redemption should be flatly denied. For as long as I can remember, the USGA has steadfastly adhered to these puritanical ideals. Whenever an errant player strays from the straight and narrow, the USGA attitude has always been that he should be punished unmercifully. In my view, however, there should always be more than one way of achieving salvation. Steadfastly, I refused to allow rough on Augusta National because I am an enthusiast of the recovery shot. It is one of the greatest pleasures in the game. In a match, a good recovery stroke can wreak havoc on an opponent and change momentum. I fear that the USGA is not an advocate of pleasure in any shape or form.

'The essential fascination of the game is watching the ball fly and waiting to see where it might end up. If the ball is hidden in deep grass and it cannot be found, let alone played, what is the point? I wanted every aspect of the Augusta course to be visible, insisting that cup positions be clearly seen from the fairway. Unlike the Calvinists of the USGA, I had the attitude that the gods of golf should look kindly on those who perform suitable acts of atonement. In golf, as well as in life, there should always be the hope of forgiveness. By all means put sinners in purgatory, but let them out if they perform good deeds. High rough is too easy an option and it spoils enjoyment.'

'I agree with you wholeheartedly!' I exclaimed, before asking, 'When did you actually decide to go after the Grand Slam?'

'The Impregnable Quadrilateral was what Grantland Rice named it. The Grand Slam came later, thanks to Bob Drumm and Arnold Palmer. For seven years I kept coming up short, but I was the same player as the one who eventually became a consistent winner. My triumphs in 1926 put it vaguely into my head that the Quadrilateral might be possible. I kept the ambition to myself though; there is too much pressure if you talk yourself up. Why I went all out for the Quadrilateral in 1930 is explained rather too simply for the Keelers of this world. I managed to win the British Amateur, which was the first major of the year; I only played in the damn thing twice for heaven's sake! When I won all of the four major titles available to me I was fulfilled, relieved and happy, ready to move on and leave the pressures of competition behind with no regrets.'

'Why was that?' I asked.

'As I've explained, I hated all the fuss. As the crowds that came out to watch my golf tournaments became larger and more unruly, I genuinely feared that one day I might kill somebody with an errant golf ball. Nor did I like northern food, apart from apple pie à la mode laced with New Jersey cream,' Jones said with a hearty chuckle.

'There were no mental gurus or sports psychologists in your day. If you had had one at your beck and call would you have won sooner?' I asked.

'Keeler was my mentor. Over and over he told me that the final act of winning is primarily a mental barrier. It took me all of seven years to cotton on. The difference between winning and losing is minuscule. Golf is a complicated, paradoxical game. There are so many different aspects to it. The long game requires athleticism, grace and power. The short game needs a delicate touch and imagination. The challenge of the mental game is to find a way to tie them both together. I know of many golfers with so-called perfect swings who never won a fiddlestick. I put it all down to a combination of fate, getting into position to win consistently, and finding a hot putter. Until I found my beloved Calamity Jane and had a long-postponed putting lesson from Walter Travis, my putting was no better than average and that one failing held me back as much as anything.'

'What is the first requisite of a sound technique?' Tail Gunner asked.

'Timing and simplicity!' Jones answered without hesitation.

'What is the best piece of advice you were ever given?' asked Tail Gunner.

'My childhood coach, Stewart Maiden, told me to hit 'em hard. They'll land somewhere! Swing slowly but hit hard, Stew said.'

'What is your happiest golfing memory and what do you like best about golf in heaven?'

'Same answer to both questions. I am able to play at Sunningdale in Surrey any time I want. In 1926 I had to pre-qualify for the Open Championship at Sunningdale. The tees were placed as far back as they could go. The par was 76. In the first round I had six 4s and three 3s on each nine. It was the most perfect golf I ever played.'

Then I heard myself asking what every golfer wants to know: 'In your opinion, Bob, what is the secret of golf success? Is it talent, technique, heart, dedication, desire or luck?'

'It is all of those plus determination, perseverance and sacrifice. Talent is the least important. Getting the most out of one's talents depends entirely on what is going on between the ears. It is not of much use to have the soundest swing in the world if you will not trust it and commit fully to the shot you are about to execute. The player must concentrate on the target and believe in himself. Ultimate success eludes many because they lack the confidence and focus to keep the game simple and believe in themselves. Golf is not really a mystery but fate does play a huge part. Many talented and dedicated golfers never make it to the top because something intangible and invisible is missing in their make-up or character.'

'Is that why golf is such a difficult game?' Tail Gunner mused.

'Golf is the only game I know that becomes more difficult the better one plays it. Some emotions are almost impossible to endure with a golf club in hand. The chief enemy of good golf is tension. I never learned anything from my victories. I got all of my best golf education from my losses.'

'How did you cope with pressure?' I asked.

'Very badly. I got sick and threw up! I come back to the same point repeatedly: the one piece of advice that always worked for me when playing under pressure was to concentrate on the target and swing the golf club as slowly as possible. And yet the paradox is that the best way to play good golf is simply to knock the hell out of the ball. Swing slowly but hit hard.'

Fascinated as Tail Gunner and I were by all this wisdom, at the same time the swirling cigarette smoke and a pair of shadowy figures that seemed to be following us in the distance were unsettling me.

'Who are those guys back there who seem to be following us?' I asked.

'Don't laugh, but those are Chick Ridley, my friend and self-appointed bodyguard, and Doc Keeler, the writer and my constant travelling companion. They both accompanied me everywhere in life. In death, they couldn't break the habit, I guess. They say it gives them something to do for eternity.'

'Why do you smoke so much, Bob? Is it because it helps to settle your nerves?'

Tail Gunner gave me a sharp elbow in the ribs. 'Are you off your rocker asking personal questions like that? Just stick to the golf, will you?' he hissed.

'I've always smoked too much. After playing with Hagen one day, Keeler wrote that The Haig went round the course in sixty-nine strokes whereas Jones took sixty-nine cigarettes! Cigarettes killed most of my family. It is, I guess, a nervous habit that causes me to light up more cigarettes than I ever finish. I light them, smoke them a bit and then throw them away. It's something to do and it helps to relieve tension. It's easy to say that cigarettes are bad for your health, but championship golf is played between the ears and being relaxed and free of tension is so important. I always felt that a smoke helped me to cope with the turmoil inside my head.'

My tee-shot's ominous drift to the right turned out to be fortunate. Inadvertently, I had taken the shortest route to the green and my ball was propped up nicely in the light rough. Because of my tight line of approach, a slight fade was needed to reach the sanctuary of a platform green, sandwiched between two sentinel dunes. Taking both my 3-metal and my courage in my hands, I let fly as hard as I could. The ball took off like a bullet, but it did not turn 'on command' and instead flew straight past the entrance to the green and plunged into a bunker.

Possibly because he was struggling to keep up with a pair of much longer hitters, Tail Gunner made an uncharacteristic error. With little hope of achieving the height to make it over the badlands with his standard low-trajectory fairway wood shot, his ball ploughed straight into the face of a fearsome bunker. It took two vicious hacks to escape. A cautious splash-out by me followed by a defensive putt to the hole-side secured my par and put me one up. What a crazy turnaround!

Bob Jones had carefully eyed up his second shot before selecting a 2-iron. He then sent the most glorious stroke soaring high into the air. At the last moment his ball banked to the right as if guided by radar and landed safely on the back half of the green, ten paces beyond the hole.

In single file we walked on to the green. As I bent down to repair Jones's pitch mark, I launched into a hymn about the magnificent shot we had just seen. When I straightened up, I noticed to my chagrin that Bob had walked through the back of the green and was heading towards the beach where the hazy figures of Ridley and Keeler were waiting. Suddenly Jones stopped, as if he had forgotten something. He turned round and, smiling broadly, beckoned us. Then he vanished.

Apprehension swamped me. Was this the end, I wondered? Had Bob Jones and Tail Gunner been sent to Doonbeg to shepherd me across the Great Divide? Tail Gunner read my thoughts and quickly reassured me. 'I know what you're thinking. Don't worry. You have plenty of earthly life left before you too become a golfing ghost. Bob Jones merely wants us to go for a paddle in the Atlantic or hit balls along the beach with him.'

As I stepped through the sea mist, thoughts from earlier in the day, when this extraordinary series of events had begun, came flooding back to me.

——— 3 ———

Good Shot Mate!

THE HIGH, altar-like first tee at Doonbeg in County Clare is one of the most dramatic puck-offs in all of golf. To gaze down the inverted funnel of jagged greens and browns is inspirational. With the sound of Atlantic waves ringing in one's ears as they crash on to the beach less than a wedge shot away, early notice is given to put one's best foot forward. Nor is there any getting away from the feeling that, from the first swing to the last, the boisterous elements of the west of Ireland will be the primary adversary.

The hearty welcome received in the clubhouse only moments earlier counts for nought once you tee it up. The course designer is the Great White Australian Shark, Greg Norman, who rose to the challenge and excelled himself in building a pure Irish links. The Shark has always played the game with enviable panache and this approach is suitably reflected at Doonbeg. Even the uproar and delays caused by objectors, who in their bid to 'save' an estimated ten million snails from the *Vertigo angustior* family, which are visible only under a microscope, could not put Greg off. In local circles the snail has been somewhat affectionately renamed Angus, probably due to the copious quantity of heifer dust that he has helped to generate.

Almost 2 miles away, the 9th green can be seen overhanging the shoreline and practically falling into the sea. Over one's left shoulder, the 18th fairway and green appear to be in a similarly precarious position. Approximately 500 yards from the tee and 50 yards from the front edge of the green, a tiny pot bunker catches one's attention. That tiny trap, no more than 6 feet wide and with magnetic powers way out of proportion to its size, dictates tactics. Behind the green, a semicircle of enormous, cone-shaped dunes makes an eye-catching backdrop. Straightaway it is obvious that Greg Norman has created a genuine golfing jewel beside Doughmore Bay.

After a lusty drive, I played a conservative lay-up with a 4-iron well short of the little trap. From a tight fairway lie, a punched 7-iron of 130 yards pitched into the heart of the ridge that runs diagonally across the green from front left to back right, then lurched sideways to a halt 15 feet past the cup. When the putt turned perfectly on cue and dived into the hole, I suspected that my first day on the Doonbeg links might be a special one.

As the crow flies, Doonbeg village is situated on a direct line equidistant between Ballybunion and Lahinch. Norman's routing is cut through a series of conical dunes adjacent to a crescent-shaped shoreline. For well over one hundred years, the sand dunes at Doonbeg have been patiently waiting for a golf course to be built on them. As long ago as 1891, this land screamed 'golf course'. Sir Alexander Shaw, a Scottish-born industrialist and golf enthusiast based in my home city of Limerick, recognized its potential. He and his friends seriously considered locating what they termed their 'summer course' here. However, the absence of an acceptable road system or, more importantly, a railway line made accessibility too difficult. Instead, one of Ireland's most intrepid golf pioneers decided to go elsewhere. To be fair, Shaw found equally good terrain 20 miles up the coast, where there was a railway service, and he became the founding father and first president of Lahinch Golf Club. Ironically, in the twenty-first century, the relative inaccessibility that stymied Shaw is now more of an attraction than an obstacle.

After my heart-lifting birdie, I marched briskly up and over the small hill on the right of the first green. Bent forward under the weight of my double-strapped carry-bag, I was startled into a bolt-upright posture by the sight of Greg Norman practice-putting solo on a wildly contoured 17th green, which is the same shape as the continent of Africa and almost as large. A caddie in his middle years, incongruously dressed in a snow-white painter's and decorator's boiler suit, was diligently supervising operations. Greg and I exchanged cursory nods. Inside my head, thoughts swirled that the task of hitting over an apparently endless sea of rough while a scary shark was cruising nearby would be beyond me.

The slightly downhill 2nd hole is a par 4 of 426 yards that plays a good deal shorter than its yardage if the prevailing southwest wind is blowing. Somehow, I managed a satisfactory contact and got the ball away safely. From behind me I heard the words, 'Good shot mate!'

To my astonishment, Norman and his caddie had walked up on to the tee beside me.

'Can I join you for a few holes, mate? I like to spend as much time as I can out on the golf course when I'm here. I have a meeting with the greens crew in about an hour so I won't be able to go too far.'

'Sure, of course,' I stuttered, my heart missing a beat. I pulled myself together to introduce myself. 'My name is Ivan Morris. I am a long-time member at Limerick, Ballybunion and Lahinch. This is my first time sampling your handiwork at Doonbeg. I must say that I've been around quite a few golfing blocks in my time, but that first hole is as good an opener as any in my experience. If the rest of the course is of the same standard, I'm in for a special treat.'

Before Norman could answer, his white-suited caddie said, 'This is a bit of an honour for you, too, Shark. Apart from being a hot-shot amateur around these parts once upon a time, this guy is a certified golf nut and the first non-American to be voted Nut of the Year by the Golf Nut Society of America!'

Until he spoke, I had not recognized Tom Churchill, Doonbeg's ever-cheerful caddie master, dressed in uniform.

After that embarrassing introduction, Greg looked at me quizzically and said, 'I wouldn't tell too many people about that dubious accolade if I were you!'

'Not a bit of it, Shark. I'm proud of being a golf nut. My wife will tell you that I could be doing a lot worse than playing golf. If I'm not at work, she always knows that I'll be on a golf course somewhere.'

Greg played his tee-shot with one of those new-fangled driving irons and our balls ended up quite close to each other near the left-hand edge of the fairway. I was able to take advantage of the architect's local knowledge. Greg told me to make certain of avoiding the cavernous sand trap that divides the entrance to a boomerang-shaped green and to use the up-slope sweep at the back of the green to my advantage.

'You must have been on a diet of magic mushrooms when you designed this green, Shark. I've never seen anything quite like it,' I remarked, as my ball ran up against the back cushion and then slowly reversed engines to work its way back down into the middle of the green.

Greg laughed. Unlike a certain Mr Hogan, 'jolly golf' did not offend Mr Norman. 'If one understands how to play angles, this is the easiest hole to birdie on the golf course,' he said, as if it were a matter of fact.

I was in no position to disagree after the Shark had engineered a tap-in birdie thanks to an exquisitely struck pitching wedge to 3 feet.

The 3rd hole is a straightaway par 4 of no more than 361 yards. Its most striking features are a swamp populated by tall reeds, a typical west of Ireland stone wall and a picturesque Irish farmhouse cottage. After hitting an exocet tee-shot that reached the narrowest part of the fairway, fifty paces short of the upslope to the raised green, the Shark took a lot for granted by commanding that I should aim for the dead centre of the fairway too. I did my best but, wary of all the trouble along the right-hand side, I pulled my ball over to the left, where it leapfrogged over the corner of a shaggy bunker and found a bare, sandy lie in the rough. Faced with a straightforward wedge to reach the putting surface, I made clumsy contact and my ball raced through the back of the tabletop green and down a steep embankment.

Now all I could see was the flag fluttering above me as my ball lay on a dirt road compacted to the consistency of concrete by the frequent footfalls of surfers going to the nearby beach. The 20 yards of ground I had to cover was inconsistent and bumpy. Thinking of what John Burke might have done in the same circumstances, I selected a 5-iron. Positioning the ball well back in my stance and gripping right down to the silver, I knuckled a low running shot along the ground. The ball hopped, skipped and jumped like a jackrabbit until it reached the brow of the slope. Once there, the ball magically changed gear, its erratic motion becoming that of a smoothly rolled putt as it glided gracefully down to the hole-side, stone dead.

Greg and Tom were struck dumb. Before we headed off to the next tee both of them attempted the same shot several times without coming remotely near my success.

'That was my John Burke knuckle shot!' I boasted with smug satisfaction as I teed up my next ball.

With a little bit of help from the prevailing south-west wind, the 4th hole (592 yards, par 5) is reachable with two of my 'Sunday-best', but to have any chance of doing so the first one had to carry over an enormous sandpit that dominates the middle of the fairway. Another stone-wall relic from Plantation days in Ireland, this one overgrown with grassy sods, protects the entrance to the green far off in the distance, as the fairway bleeds seamlessly through a gap in the wall to join the rumpled surface, which resembles a rug carelessly thrown out on the grass to dry.

'I always look for as much variety as possible in my green sites and include as many different characteristics as I possibly can, putting some up on plateaux, some down in hollows and others on the same flat level as the fairway. I detest predictable point-to-point, dart-board golf,' said Greg, reading my thoughts.

My wind-assisted drive barely scrambled over the huge sand-pit, putting me in 'POMO' – position of maximum opportunity. From there, a sweeping right-to-left fairway metal that skirted past several pot bunkers and raced through the gap in the sod wall. Despite my frantic shouts of 'Stop!', the ball kept on running through the back left-hand corner into a shallow swale. A firm swish with the Texas Wedge followed, sending my Pro-V1 scurrying over the waves of tightly mown grass to within 3 feet of the can. I could feel Norman's hawk-like, pale-blue eyes boring right through the back of my head as I bolted the little putt home before nerves got the better of me.

'Four, four, four, four – pretty darn neat for a nut, mate!' said the beaming Shark, who had launched a soaring drive well over 300 yards before chicken-winging a 4-iron shot of the highest quality on to the green for his matching birdie.

The drive from the 5th tee (373 yards, par 4) goes uphill through an angled gap in the dunes on to the seat of a saddle fairway.

'What surprises have you in store for me up there, Greg?' I enquired.

'Hit it 210 dead centre and you'll be perfect. Into the breeze, that should be one of your fairway metals, I imagine.'

Thanks to a boost of adrenaline, I hit my ball one yard too far: 210 would have been perfect; 212 would have been as dead as a doornail; my 211 was barely playable. These superstars are mighty precise with their yardages, I thought silently. Greg was tickled pink when he saw my ball hanging precariously on the edge of a deep pit of unruly grass in the dead centre of the fairway.

'One yard more and you would need a stepladder to play that one,' he giggled.

'One yard less, dammit, and I would have been perfect,' I growled back.

Effectively standing on one leg and gripping well down the handle of my 9-iron, I aimed vaguely in the direction of the green and swung as hard as I could before stumbling backwards on to my backside. The ball came out low and hot, and ricocheted off the side of a dune before chasing forward, up a slope, into the centre of the green. Another fluke! Greg played a superbly controlled 7-iron. At no stage was the ball more than 20 feet off the ground. The initial velocity was so fast that I thought the ball would fly over everything and land in the ocean, but it suddenly lost momentum, touched down on top of a large bump near the back of the green and sucked sharply backwards. My conscience must have been bothered by the undeserved birdie opportunity, because I made a very timid attempt. Greg's more positive effort also missed.

A serpentine walk through the dunes to the 6th tee gave us an opportunity to chat. We discussed wildlife issues and how they can be enhanced by golf. I told Greg about the natterjack toad population in County Kerry, which was under threat a few years ago; its survival was of grave concern. To everyone's delight, a golf course close to the natterjack's dwindling breeding grounds has facilitated the revitalization of the species rather than causing its elimination. By building small lakes with shallow tapered edges, a few hundred toads have become thousands within a few years. Dr Arthur Spring, an Irish golf architect, who took the same career path as Dr Alister Mackenzie by abandoning a medical practice to satisfy his passion for golf, had noticed that the toads were spawning in seasonal rain pools. Most of the babies died as soon as the water evaporated in spring. The permanent water gave the toads a more secure refuge and a better chance to metamorphose.

'Golf courses can be havens for flora and fauna if managed properly,' I explained. 'A golf course is a far safer place for plant life than lands that are grazed by cattle or sheep. But who objects to the damage that they cause? The fear of fertilizer over-use on golf courses is greatly exaggerated. Golf courses use a fraction of the chemicals that are used in agriculture, particularly when grass is grown for silage. Hedgerows and trees that are cultivated as hazards on so many golf courses are completely safe habitats for birds and insects. Besides, the actual playing area that is trodden by golfers during the course of a game is a fraction of the total amount of land needed to build a golf course. Rather than harming it, golf does a lot of good for the environment.'

This was all said with more passion than was necessary because I was preaching to the converted.

The raised back tee at the 6th (370 yards, par 4) overlooks the beach and the fairway runs from a deep, hidden bowl between unruly dunes through an ascending valley parallel to the shoreline. The slightest of hooks will end up on the beach; any miss to the right will result in an ungainly hack-out or a lost ball. From the back tee, it is the most unnerving shot on the golf course.

Greg teed up quickly and let fly with his driver. The bright blue shaft flashed in the sunlight and his ball flew as straight as an arrow, coming to a halt so close to the green's edge that he could have side-footed on. The sound of the strike as titanium and urethane met gave me shudders. Daring not even to think about trying to emulate such a prodigious strike, I asked if I could borrow the hybrid club that Greg had used so impressively off the 2nd and 5th tees. Instead of tearing at my swing and unsettling me, the wind was my friend on this occasion: it assisted my ball to fade gently into the dead centre of the fairway, albeit a full 100 yards behind Greg's.

'Good shot mate! Did you ever consider coming out and joining me on the Champions Tour?' chuckled my playing companion, tongue firmly planted in cheek. 'And thank you for letting me play along with you, mate! I would absolutely love to stay out here with you for the rest of the round but I have to go now. Before leaving I felt like I had to hit one final driver shot up that fairway – it's one of my favourites on the golf course. You may keep the hybrid – the club obviously suits you – but will you please return my ball to the Pro Shop? I may need it again next time I'm here.'

'Gosh! Thanks very much, Greg. It was a thrill and a privilege to be allowed to observe such a magnificent exhibition of ball-striking at close quarters. I look forward to playing with you again sometime,' I said, taken aback.

We shook hands, then Greg and his caddie turned and strode smartly away in the direction of the clubhouse.

The highest part of the 6th green is its front edge; everything from that point meanders downwards in erratic steps for 120 feet or thereabouts. After hitting a glorious (for me) 9-iron second shot to the back edge of the green and securing another regulation par, my heart was singing.

Going to the next tee, I realized that I had found the elusive zone that one hears experts like Ewan Murray and Bruce Critchley of Sky Sports discussing on TV. For the first time in many years I was achieving my potential. It was a good feeling to know I was focusing properly, visualizing the flight of the ball clearly and thinking only of the target, while being locked into that much-sought-after process of playing one shot at a time. A rare unity between mind and body gave me an inner calm and confidence that I have experienced all too rarely. Too late in my career, I had learnt that it is only when the mind and body work in unison that one is in a position to play at one's peak. For years, I had striven in vain to force my body to bend to my will. Now, at last, I was playing reactively, allowing my subconscious feelings and instincts to freewheel and dictate events.

4

The Doonbeg Ghost

T HE 7TH IS LOCATED in the heart of the golf course. A glance at the scorecard reveals a formidable par 3 measuring a whopping 227 yards from the back marker. Because the tee is considerably elevated, only the slightest hint of the prevailing breeze from the south-west ensures that the hole plays nowhere near that length. The entrance to the green is receptively open and flat: as good as his word, Norman provides another opportunity for weaker players to run balls on to the putting surface. 'The ball is made round so that it will roll as well as fly,' Greg had told me.

More earth was moved at the 7th than on any other part of the golf course, but one would never know it. The secluded amphitheatre of man-made dunes appears totally natural.

As I was considering my club selection, I became vaguely aware of two figures standing behind the green. One of them wore a flat, woollen cap and had a pencil-slim golf bag slung casually across his shoulder. My concentration level was locked tight into 'the zone', so I easily dismissed this unexpected intrusion and carried on with my pre-shot routine. A raking 3-iron shot swooped on to the apron and released 20 yards forward, before skidding to a halt about one third of the way into the putting surface. When I holed the curling putt of 35 feet for my third birdie of the day, I accepted it with a modest shrug and glanced sheepishly in the general direction of the two onlookers.

'I always said that you could putt with a sweeping brush, never mind that fancy-looking Harold Swash dude. Three under after 7 isn't too shabby for a has-been warhorse.'

I froze to the spot, because the nasal rasp was immediately recognizable. The vision of my much-missed lifetime pal, James 'Tail Gunner' Carew, was grinning broadly at me. I was thrown into a state of utter confusion and it took several seconds before my senses were regained.

Then, with a spring in my step, I strode towards him. 'Is Doonbeg as good as the golf in heaven?' I demanded to know.

'It certainly is, and I hope you are enjoying every minute of it,' the ghost answered.

'Are you going to introduce me to your friend?' I asked, curious to find out who the ghost-person, whom I did not recognize, standing beside Tail Gunner might be.

'This is Arnold Haultain, who, in 1908, wrote the first and probably still the best metaphysical study of golf.'

'How do you do? James has told me about your devotion to the royal and ancient game. I would be intrigued to find out why you like golf so much?' asked Haultain in a refined Oxbridge accent.

You would think that a certified golf nut would have a ready-made, stock answer to that question, but possibly because a ghost had posed it I was unable to organize my thoughts and remained awkwardly tongue-tied.

Tail Gunner came to my assistance, saying, 'Golf is endlessly fascinating and never boring. Right down to the simple act of being able to walk around in the countryside surrounded by the beauty of nature, it is always a joy. Every golfing day is different. The goalposts are always being moved; the examination paper is continually being altered. No player, no matter how skilled, can duplicate a specific sequence of shot-making, let alone replicate a round of golf. I see golf courses as sculptured landscapes, fine works of art on the same level as marble-walled museums. Nor do the landscapes happen accidentally. All of the great golf-course architects have striven to incorporate as much artistic merit into their designs as is humanly possible. The chief object of every golf architect is to imitate nature so closely as to make his work indistinguishable from nature herself. I have not the slightest hesitation in saying that beauty means a great deal on a golf course; even the man who states he does not care for beauty because he only wants 'good golf' is subconsciously influenced by his surroundings.'

At last, I felt sufficiently composed to join in the debate. 'It is one of the paradoxes of the game that, initially, many of us like golf because it is an individual sport. To enjoy being at one with oneself and one's surroundings is a part of golf I learned early. And yet, one of the most pleasant, valuable and long-lasting consequences of the game is the wonderful, lifetime friendships we make. This is the most sociable of games, on and off the golf course.

'Some wag said that golf is ninety per cent mental and the other ten per cent is in the mind. At the highest echelons, the emphasis on the mental game cannot be over-emphasized, because good technique and accurate ball-striking are taken for granted. Go to any professional tournament, sit close to the practice ground and watch the players going through their routines. On the evidence before them, I defy anybody to pick out who will return the best score. Once the game begins, it doesn't take long for the brain to come into play and that is what separates out those who will do best as the day gets under way.

'Those who believe that a golf ball does not know what hit it and that it will invariably react to the empirical laws of physics are technically correct, but they are actually deluding themselves. It may be possible to explain scientifically everything about a golf ball's flight, but it will not help much in the heat of battle when calm, clear thinking counts more than accurate ball-striking. Some misguided enthusiasts analyse every tiny movement and contortion of the golf swing. They are always on the lookout for a "secret" that will elevate their performances, but they will be wasting their time if they have not got the right attitude.' I felt quite pleased with my contribution to this rather intellectual conversation.

'Golf is a source of distraction, consolation and fulfilment,' Tail Gunner added, 'and golf courses are welcome respites from all the trials, tribulations and irritations of life. When you play golf you are forced to concentrate so hard that all your problems are forgotten for a few hours. The greatest joy comes from playing to your full potential every now and again. Even the most successful players do not win very often. Now there's a thought: perhaps the most successful golfers are the least satisfied and contented ones? Professor Haultain said as much when he captured the essence of the game as succinctly as anyone has ever done in his book *The Mystery of Golf.*'

'Well, thank you most kindly for saying so,' replied Haultain. 'After much foolish resistance, I took to golf at the relatively advanced age of forty-one and therefore I never became an accomplished player. However, it did not take long before I was writing in my journal: "Would someone please tell wherein lies the extraordinary fascination with golf? I have just come home from my club. We played until we could no longer see the flag. The caddies were sent ahead to find the balls by the thud of their fall. A large, low moon threw whispering shadows on the dew-swept grass, ere we trod the home green. At dinner the talk was of golf, and for three hours after dinner, the talk was of golf. Yet the talkers were neither fools nor monomaniacs. We were (merely) probing and elucidating the profundities of the game."

'Thanks to my training in psychology and biology, I was able to construct some hypotheses. I recognized that the difficulties of the game concerned the workings of an individual's mind and nervous system, rather than the relatively simple task of hitting a small ball around a large field. While golf is unquestionably a game of precision and skill, the duffer can, out of the blue, conceive and execute a single sublime stroke equal in purity to the best player in his club. On the other hand, the likes of a Ben

Hogan will tell you that he feels lucky if he manages to play four or five shots in a round exactly as he had planned. Such paradoxes make the game an intoxicating challenge for everybody. The joy of seeing that pristine white globe fly at the target as one envisaged never diminishes. A game of raw power, balletic beauty and machine-like precision one minute changes to one demanding a hypersensitive and delicate touch the next.'

I broke in again to say, 'Another aspect of the game, which goes largely unnoticed by those who have never subjected themselves to serious competition, is that nerves and courage are usually tested in a completely private way. Only the player himself will be fully aware of the real moments of triumph and disaster that can occur during a competitive round of golf. Even one's playing companions might not appreciate when one has been lucky or the opposite, or if demons of doubt have been overcome to achieve the minor triumph of a bogey salvaged, or the psychological difficulty that causes a straightforward putt to be fluffed because of its significance as a personal benchmark.'

Now in full flow, I continued, 'Golf can be played with ferocious intensity or carefree abandon. One's frame of mind can enhance or impede performance to an amazing degree. I know of no other game that encompasses such wide-ranging combinations of mental application, physical skill and luck. Those who have played the game for a long time regard the astonishing and unpredictable nature of golf as normal. In a nutshell, golf is never boring.'

Both Haultain and Tail Gunner had listened intently as we walked along the path through the dunes towards the next tee. Then Tail Gunner changed the subject.

'The pleasure of playing here at Doonbeg was never an option during my lifetime. So I was bursting with curiosity to see how the course had turned out. From what I have seen, I would definitely have become a member here, if only I had lived long enough. The course plays beautifully and it is so convenient to Kilkee, where I used to spend my summer vacations. I would not have been able to resist being up here every afternoon.'

'You certainly picked a beautiful afternoon to come,' I enthused.

'Of course I did! Ghosts do not play in the rain,' he answered, his impish grin to the fore once more.

With Haultain lagging behind, distracted by the sight of a wild orchid, the chit-chat continued unabated until we reached the 8th tee (582 yards, par 5). Tail Gunner told me that the hole I was about to tackle was a test of power and strategy – a fairly typical example of how Dr Alister Mackenzie had influenced his profession. He explained that Mackenzie was the first intentionally to embrace camouflage and deception as a concept in course design. Following this example, Greg Norman had made the judgement of line and distance at Doonbeg a subtle challenge.

I was then able to tell Tail Gunner about my earlier experience of playing with Greg Norman. I said that Norman was far from being the flat-out, one-gear player I had thought him to be. In fact, he possessed all the shots necessary to play in the windy west of Ireland.

Standing on the tee waiting for Professor Haultain to catch up with us, Tail Gunner described the tactics applicable to the next hole I was about to play.

'A conservative, short-hitting player may plot his way along the relatively open right-hand side largely unhindered. It is clearly a longer but safer route, with only a few fairway obstacles in his line of fire. The long-hitter who decides to embrace the shorter, more direct, left-hand route will have several serious hazards to play over. Of course, if he overcomes them there should be the reward of a birdie. Mind you, there is nothing intrinsically wrong with the fact that long-hitters should have an advantage, but the constant stretching of yardage that appears to have been going on since I left destroys the fun for short-hitting players. If a short-hitter cannot win once in a while, the game is the poorer for it. Another less obvious discrepancy that leads to conflict and provides unsolvable conundrums for course architects is that pros rarely worry about trouble on their flanks. Their primary concern is to hit the ball the correct yardage. On the other hand, the overriding challenge for average golfers is to steer a straight course,' Tail Gunner said wistfully.

'This is just like old times!' I said. 'I haven't had a golf chat like this since you departed. But enough of that for now: I would prefer to talk to you about it later, because I have a good round going and I don't want to lose the rare chance of doing a low score.' I flexed my muscles as I prepared to launch my next boomer. I was terrified that if I thought about anything other than the process of executing my next shot I would lose the magic touch.

'Typical!' said the ghost. 'You haven't changed. Will you ever learn not to try so hard? You're always pressurizing yourself, causing unnecessary anxiety and tension. When will you learn to play without expectation? Instead of focusing your energy on achieving a self-imposed target, you should simply enjoy the game. Piling pressure on to your own shoulders is madness. Putting ambition on a pedestal is a mistake. The object of the game should be enjoyment. Whenever you manage to win a tournament or reach a personal milestone, it should be regarded as no more than a bonus.'

Tail Gunner had insinuated himself so seamlessly into my game that playing golf with a ghost felt normal. He directed me to the blue (back) tee saying, 'That's 246 yards of carry to test you. I'm going to hit from the white tees because my equipment isn't up to playing from all the way back there.'

I looked into the ghost's bag and saw a familiar red-headed 1970s Spalding ceramic-headed driver with a lovely black and white insert and matching 4-wood; a half set of Wilson LT 1200 irons; a 1940s blade putter by Forgan of Leven with a brown Apollo shaft.

'I'm playing with the small ball too,' he remarked, showing me a sparkling new Penfold Patented, stamped with a red Ace of Diamonds, which he had carefully removed from a bright blue wax-paper wrapper.

'I haven't seen one of those for thirty-odd years! That lump of soap will go nowhere!' I exclaimed.

'We'll see,' said the ghost.

Facing up to the task of hitting over a no-man's land that in Florida would be an alligator- and snake-infested swamp, I widened my stance, stretched out my backswing and let fly. My timing was good. The ball rose quickly and soared over the trouble. Tail Gunner went 50 yards forward and made his brisk, tidy swing, which I remembered so well. Haultain declined to play along with us, saying that he would prefer to ramble in the rough looking for more orchids.

On reaching my ball, I began considering my options. Tail Gunner joined me to give me the benefit of his wisdom. 'Maybe by some miracle of modern technology you might get close to the green in two if you take on the shorter, more heroic route along the left, but you will be bringing a high number into the frame if you fail.'

Accepting his advice, I endeavoured to play safely out to the right-hand side of the fairway with my newly acquired hybrid club. Instead, I stone cold topped the ball. It ran along the ground like a terrified rabbit, burying itself under the lip of a deep fairway bunker. From there, I could do no more than make a despairing chop sideways on to the fairway with my sand-wedge.

Now, 100 yards from the front edge of the green and with Tail Gunner already safely on board the elevated plateau green in three, I stood over my ball, fingering my arsenal and musing silently: 'Float the wedge or run it up the incline with a 7-iron?'

Tail Gunner seemed to be enjoying my indecisiveness. He knew that confusion would inevitably cause a lethal lack of self-trust.

After much procrastination, I plumped for the aerial route and played my wedge. The ball ballooned into the headwind, landing 6 inches short of safety, spinning inexorably backwards into a deep trough in front of the green. From there I chipped far too aggressively, 20 feet past the flag. Two putts resulted in an extremely untidy seven blows. I turned puce and was about to throw my putter in the general direction of the next tee when I heard a gentle 'Tsk, tsk' from the lips of the ghost.

Instead, I froze my javelin action and settled for slamming the innocent implement back into its scabbard with a resounding thud.

'So much for playing safe. I may as well have had the satisfaction of attacking that second shot and be damned one way or the other!' I snarled.

My zone of confident concentration had not lasted long. My brain was now in turmoil, scrambled by a tiny mistake that had undermined my equilibrium. Two strokes down to a flipping ghost playing with 1960s equipment – damn, heifer dust and fiddlesticks!

--- 5 ---

Sir Alex and Old Tom

T HANKS TO THOSE seven clumsy blows, my *que será, será* attitude flip-flopped disastrously. All my carefully garnered momentum evaporated into the clear Clare air as a destructive, fighting-cock disposition took over. I should have known that this approach needed to be dismissed at once, but losing composure at inopportune moments has always been a self-defeating tendency of mine. The unavoidable outcome of inner demons consuming the golfer is ignominious failure. Too often my golfing misfortunes have been self-inflicted.

The troublestrewn 9th hole (175 yards) is one place where aggression is superfluous to requirements. Two paces from the left edge of the green, a rickety, somewhat askew, out-of-bounds fence, in imminent danger of falling on to the beach 15 feet below, clings precariously to the golf course. Over to the right-hand side, four riveted pot bunkers and a gnarly rough lie in wait for any misdirected or cowardly strokes. My scrambled brain rendered me incapable of finessing my next swing, although I did manage enough presence of mind to remember a pearl of wisdom that I had learned from a wise old Irish pro named Denis Cassidy.

'When there is mortal danger on the left, young fella, hang on hard with your left hand and bate the 'buckin' ball!' he had said.

Tail Gunner held the honour and, selecting a 5-iron, he threaded a low tracer bullet straight as a die through the narrow entrance on to the centre of the green. In attempting to 'nuke' a 7-iron, I allowed my lower body to lean slightly in front of the point of contact and my ball flew a couple of yards offline to the right. It dumped into a diabolically conceived bunker where I had barely enough room to make a stance let alone swing a golf club. It was as much as I could do to blast out to safety. A gallant but unsuccessful putt followed. Three down.

When we reached the 10th tee we were treated to a strange spectacle in choreography. Two elderly gentlemen, dressed in heavy, woollen tweed suits and flat caps, each of them clasping hickory-shafted clubs behind their backs, were zigzagging erratically down the fairway in front of us, lost in conversation. The momentary delay gave me just enough precious seconds to recover my senses.

The 10th (580 yards, par 5) runs across the top end of the links, perpendicular to the rest of the course. From a cramped tee box that is pushed into a corner between a small dune and the course boundary, I found the line of play to be ill-defined. Standing there for the first time, I couldn't fully appreciate the dangers lying ahead of me. A series of sod-wall traps, which cannot be seen when standing on the tee, litter the left-hand rough. Only slightly further to the left is a stone wall indicating the course boundary. Also out of sight but over to the right, a 6-foot-wide, reed-infested stream lies in wait for any sliced tee-shots. The stream crosses the fairway diagonally at 270 yards from the tee, tightly hugging the left-hand edge of the fairway on its journey to the green-side. If the drive is troublestrewn, the second shot is risk-and-reward stuff to the nth degree. The entrance to the green is as narrow as the eye of a needle, flanked on the left by the already-mentioned stream, while over on the right there is high grass, brambly bushes and half a dozen unkempt bunkers overgrown with marram.

After a goodish drive, my well-struck 3-metal second shot appeared as if it might have come to rest on top of a knoll overlooking the hidden putting surface, which is down in a dell.

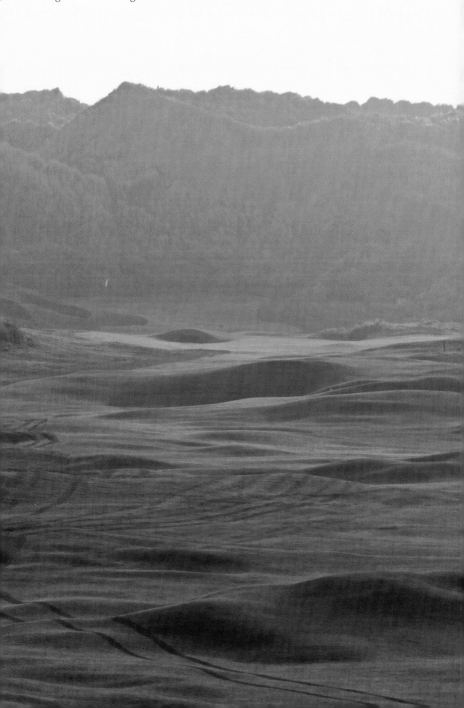

Doonbeg 1st (par 5) An early-morning view of how the player 'sees' the second shot at Doonbeg's 1st hole. The barely visible pot bunker in front of the green is substantially foreshortened in this photograph, being fifty paces from the front edge. Any ball that comes within 20 yards of this nasty piece of work will be sucked into its nether regions by an invisible gravitational magnet.

▲ **Doonbeg 8th (par 5)** The bunker-strewn approach to the 8th green. The large trap on the right looks less menacing in print than it is in reality. Stay well clear or you will be chopping out sideways.

▼ **Doonbeg 12th (par 4)** An overhead view of the quixotic trap deposited by Norman in the middle of the 12th green at Doonbeg. The player approaches from the left, as we look at this photo, which renders the trap completely hidden from view until one walks on to the surface of the green.

▼ **Doonbeg 14th (par 3)** The dramatic 111-yard 14th at Doonbeg requires both precision and nerves of steel when it is played directly into the prevailing south-west wind.

Doonbeg 6th (par 4) and 13th (par 5) An unusual crossover junction between the back tee at the 6th and 13th green that is typical of Greg Norman's Doonbeg! Norman did not allow such a quaint design oddity to deter him from presenting one of the most demanding and memorable tee-shots on the entire links at this location. Doughmore Beach on the left is very much in play and has been visited by golf balls belonging to the author on several occasions.

▲ **Lahinch (Old) 6th (par 4)** The author rather immodestly claims to have assisted the architect in the selection of the site for the 6th green at Lahinch. The original plan presented to an EGM in 1999 had the new 6th green in a depression near where the path ends, well to the right of where it was eventually built. Martin Hawtree graciously accepted the suggestion made from the floor 'to put the green up on the knoll where the 8th tee used to be.' Dare we suggest that the new 6th is one of the acknowledged successes of Hawtree's 'Mackenzieization' of Lahinch Old?

▲ **Enniscrone 14th (par 5)** The infamous dune named Cnoc na gCorp (*background*) has nasty stories told about it and I do not mean tales of the many stray golf balls it has snatched. Underneath it, legend says, are buried hundreds of Vikings slain by the O'Dowda clan in a bloody battle in AD 789 at Killala Bay close by. The dune, arguably the tallest on any golf course in Ireland, looms eerily over a plunging fairway valley that leads straight-hitting golfers in single file to the 14th green (*foreground*) at Enniscrone.

▼ **Royal County Down (Championship) 1st (par 5)** The spectacularly beautiful but quirky 1st hole at Royal County Down where a drive and a wedge one day can become three metal clubs and something else added the next! In certain conditions the golf ball can roll 'for miles' at RCD but never in a straight line. If the shot is blind in the first instance, finding one's golf ball can be an adventure in itself.

▲ **Waterville 2nd (par 4)** The surroundings are typically Kerry: forty shades of green, cyan water, purple mountains and saffron gorse abound. What bunkers? Steer a course along the left hand side of the deceptively wide fairway and any unwanted visits to the sand will be avoided.

▼ **The European 17th (par 4)** The 17th hole at Pat Ruddy's European Club is truly heavenly. It is a golf hole fit for the likes of a Tom Watson (in whose honour it is dedicated) and Bob Jones, not ordinary mortals. The drive down into the valley is thrilling but the uphill second with a mid or long iron has to be struck with authority.

Instead, to my chagrin, I found my ball playing hide-and-go-seek in a dark corner of a large bunker. Once again, there was no way forward. I was forced to waste a shot and play out sideways. A speculative wedge stroke followed, fortuitously coming to rest 9 feet past the cup. With all the determination I could muster, I rolled in the putt for a hard-earned half in par as Tail Gunner steered a serene, regulation course through all the trouble. Still three down.

We could still hear the waves crashing 250 yards away as we walked to the elevated 11th tee (148 yards, par 3), the furthest point from the sea on the course. But I had no interest in that. I was concerned only with how I might overcome the three-stroke deficit as rapidly as possible.

Up first, Tail Gunner selected a 6-iron, but into the stiff wind it was never going to be enough club and his ball dug its toes into the turf on the green apron and agonizingly rolled 20 yards backwards to the base of the steep upslope in front of the elevated green. I also chose a 6-iron. Swinging as hard as I could to make sure that I cleared the yawning mouth of an enormous sand bunker, my ball flew over that obstacle but, on landing in the centre of the green, escaped my control and disappeared over the back of the green.

Tail Gunner was famous all over Ireland for his short-game skills, but he misjudged the steepness of the incline on this occasion and his ball pulled up 15 feet short of the cup. Back in the 1960s, long before Phil Mickelson was born, a Ballybunionite named Brendan Houlihan – whom the members there affectionately called 'th'aul pro' – taught me the parachute shot. Sharp wrist work arched my ball into a high parabola; it landed softly, and gingerly rolled up against the flagstick before sliding staccato-style to the bottom of the cup. Tail Gunner just missed his putt. Two strokes recovered in one fell swoop. Now one down. Game on.

As I bent to pick up my golf bag, I caught a sideways glimpse of four black, highly polished hobnail boots. They belonged to the two gentlemen whom we had seen walking down the 10th fairway.

'That was a bonnie wee ferret, laddie!' said the more senior of the two, who sported a bushy white beard.

'Thank you!' I replied without looking at his face properly.

'What's a ferret?' I heard myself asking as my curiosity suddenly got the better of me. It was only then that I recognized the smiling faces of Old Tom Morris and Sir Alex Shaw. Both of them appeared to have been charmed to witness my small slice of golfing magic.

'Och, a ferret is a chip-in from the side of the green, laddie. A golden ferret is holing out from a green-side bunker. D'ye not ken that in third millennium gawf?' said Old Tom.

Totally speechless, I could not even stammer a reply. Every golfer knows about the seminal part that Old Tom Morris played in the development of golf in Scotland, but not so many know about his contributions to Irish golf too.

Sir Alex Shaw was the intrepid pioneer who brought the royal and ancient game to my part of the world. In 1886 he built a course for his private use at Kilkee, only 6 miles from where we were standing. He was also the prime mover behind the establishment of Limerick and Lahinch Golf Clubs in the early 1890s. Both Tail Gunner and I were very interested in making his acquaintance.

Born in Scotland in 1848, Shaw made his home in Limerick thirty years later and spent the rest of his life there. As the founder and owner of the once thriving Shaw's Bacon Factory, he became one of Limerick's most successful and wealthy merchant princes.

Shaw had the Midas touch in business and he was more than willing to share his good fortune with the citizens of his adopted city. During his lifetime he made many laudable contributions to local society. He supported a wide spectrum of charitable works, and applied his philanthropy and brainpower to a plethora of commercial, artistic and sporting pursuits. As well as his entrepreneurial spirit, Shaw was a man of culture: he was a lifetime member of the exclusive Royal Academy and also of the Royal College of Music. He served as a governor of Barrington's Hospital and as a director of Limerick Chamber of Commerce, while also being the principal shareholder in the Waterford, Limerick and Western Railway Company, which was useful when attempting to entice golfers from all over Ireland and Britain to travel to Lahinch. But it was as the benevolent father of the game of golf in the region that he left his most telling and long-lasting mark. All in all, he was a most likeable personality. For his many services to his community, King Edward VII knighted Alex Shaw in 1906.

Around 1880, on one of his occasional trips home to Scotland, Shaw visited the town of St Andrews and was persuaded to try his hand at the new sporting phenomenon that was sweeping the land. There he was introduced to none other than Old Tom Morris, the acknowledged master of all things pertaining to the game, and he took a series of lessons and purchased a set of custom-made, hickory-shafted clubs from Tom. The two men became firm friends.

The Shaws spent their summer vacations at the west Clare seaside village of Kilkee, as many Limerick families still do. After his visit to St Andrews, Shaw had caught the golfing bug and was restless to try the game again. For a while he remained content with standing atop the cliffs known as George's Head, practising his swing. The natives probably thought that he had taken leave of his senses – especially as Shaw had been instructed by Old Tom to practise without the distraction of a ball.

'Mr Shaw is up on George's Head flailing at fresh air with a walking stick!' somebody said, mystified, shaking his head over a pint of stout in Scott's Bar.

But Shaw ignored the wags; he had ears only for Old Tom's gentle burr, whispering to him, 'If ye can concentrate on findin' a guid bawlanced finish tae the gawf swing, what went afore will hae tae be passable execution. At aw times strive tae let the wee baw get in the way o' the swing, nae mair, nae less.'

It was excellent advice, but nobody at Kilkee in the mid-1880s had any idea what the purpose of Shaw's flailing might be. How could anybody have known that one of golf's greatest evangelists had inspired him to behave in such a manner? Shaw never became more than an average player, but he was devoted to prose-lytizing the game in his adopted country. As an unfulfilled golfer and pragmatic businessman, he was a good example of the type of person Arnold Haultain wrote about in *The Mystery of Golf*:

> The game is beyond reason. You may speculate in stocks; you may lay odds on a horse race; but the money market and the turf are child's play compared with the uncertainties of golf; on the links it is (only) your own individual effort that counts. My opponent had a bad night; or so he dolefully told me, and he fully expected defeat. What was the result? His best ever round on the links! Golf is not amenable to reason.

I looked around, straining to see if the author of those words was close enough to be called over and included in our conversation, but he was nowhere to be seen.

After returning from one of his trips to St Andrews, Shaw decided to lay out a home-made course above the cliffs at Kilkee's west end. It may have been a crude construction with an un-defined number of holes, but it was the beginning of golf in north Munster. Kilkee Golf Club did not become properly organized and constituted until 1896, but Shaw and his close associates were playing the game informally for about ten years before that date.

In 1890, the famous Scottish Black Watch Regiment arrived in Limerick to take up garrison duties on behalf of Her Majesty's Government. Several of them were expert golfers. Without delay, Shaw enlisted their help in the building of a proper golf course near Limerick city. The principal officers involved were Messers Deane and Carter, both scratch golfers, and Messers Elton and McFarlane, who were only slightly less accomplished. Shaw directed and financed them to put both their expertise at golf and their knowledge of military engineering to good use. Within one year, Limerick Golf Club was to become only the third golf club outside Ulster to be legally constituted in Ireland.

In 1892, Shaw and his military colleagues, along with Messers Richard Plummer, John Barrington and Joseph Matterson (all from Limerick), founded Lahinch Golf Club. They called it their 'summer links by the sea'. For the first two years of its existence, the same group of people that ran Limerick Golf Club, 50 miles inland, managed the affairs of Lahinch too.

Prior to Shaw and his friends deciding to locate at Lahinch, they considered using sites at Kilrush and Doonbeg. The latter had to wait for another hundred years and the arrival of a Great White Shark; a golf course was founded at Kilrush in 1934.

Almost immediately, Shaw appreciated Lahinch's potential and he set about realizing it. From that point onwards, Lahinch Golf Club became the main focus of his attention and Shaw devoted much of his time and energy to the development of both club and village. He remained in office as executive president of the club until his death in 1923 at the age of seventy-five.

A determined and persistent man, Alex Shaw believed in aiming high. In 1894, during one of his regular trips to Scotland, he managed to persuade Old Tom Morris – much against the wishes of the Scottish maestro's wife – to travel to Ireland at Shaw's expense to advise on the layout of a golf links that would be 'second to none'. Morris spent three happy months at Lahinch, strolling about the course, often in the company of Shaw, with his favourite cleek or mashie clasped behind his back. They hit balls along imaginary fairways while they plotted and planned. Morris was in no hurry to complete the task. He enjoyed Shaw's lavish hospitality and chatting with the local people he met in the pubs he visited.

In the evenings, Morris often held court in a small public house on the Main Street owned by the O'Dwyer family. In 1964, seventy years later, golf cartoonist and author George Haughton visited the little pub, now named The 19th. Haughton was flabbergasted when an elderly Mary O'Dwyer told him that she could remember as a young girl serving whiskey and stout to Old Tom and speaking to him as intimately as if he were her grandad.

'He was lovely man to chat with,' she told Haughton.

Gradually, the golf course of Shaw's dreams emerged – but only just in time, before one of Tom's daughters arrived from Scotland, sent over to march her dilettante father back home to his irate wife. Morris was deeply impressed by the dunes at Lahinch and upon his return to the 'home of golf' declared to anybody who would listen that the links that he and Shaw had built on the west coast of Ireland was 'the equal of anything in Scotland'. Such praise was to be exploited to its fullest extent by Shaw.

Dinner-table discussions between Shaw and Morris, which often took place in Sherry's Hotel, just up the road from O'Dwyer's Pub on the Main Street, would have included a golf lesson or two and the birth of a few ideas for the development of the village into the fully blown 'St Andrews of Ireland' golf resort that it has become. When the claret and whiskey flowed, Old Tom could talk up a storm. His vast experience of developing the game in Scotland was expertly brain-picked by an astute fellow-countryman.

'Tom, I have enjoyed your presence tremendously, and being able to play golf with you every day. But in spite of your lessons, I am frustrated by my lack of progress. It is only in the last few days that the quality of my stroke has begun to show improvement. What should I do to maintain my form when you have gone home to St Andrews?'

'Mr Shaw, sir, you are a busy man. Normally, you do not have time to play golf more than once a week. Nor are you as young and as flexible as you once were. From one week to the next your golfing muscles stiffen up from lack of use. I suggest that you combat this by keeping a heavy club close by at all times, in your office and beside your bed, or wherever is convenient. You should swing that heavy club for at least five minutes every morning and every evening. Start by using both hands on the club, but always take a few swings with each arm separately before you finish. Stretch out as much as you can without striking the chandeliers! Find a nice balanced finish to your swing and hold it for ten seconds. If you feel you must have something to hit, roll up a paper ball: that way you won't break anything and Mrs Shaw won't be after your blood!'

'That sounds good. I'll do that! Now tell me how in blazes can I stop that dreadful topped shot that kills me stone dead at least twice in every round I play?'

'You mean instead of sending the ball clean away you hit the top of the ball and drive it straight into the ground? At St Andrews we call that "foundering the ball". It might be the most damaging shot in golf. It would be better to hit fresh air. What could be worse than missing the ball completely? And yet when a ball is missed, the perpetrator escapes at the cost of a single stroke, whereas the foundered ball almost always dives into the direst of trouble, costing the player far more than one stroke.'

Tom Morris continued his dinner-table lesson. 'You are picking the club up too straight and too high from the ball and coming straight down on top of it. You need to widen your swing by dragging the club back along the ground as far as you can before turning your shoulders and back to the target completely. If you do this you will also achieve maximum distance in the hit. Of course, you must never move your head or alter the angle of your spine while you are swinging back. Excuse me for saying this, sir, but keep your belly button facing the butt end of the golf club at all times and try to turn without moving the centre of your body backwards or forwards. Swing the arms back and around while keeping the body as still as you can. One final piece of advice: point the club shaft at the target at the top of the backstroke and do exactly the same at the finish of the swing.'

'I will strive earnestly to remember that. Now tell me, Tom, how will we get people to come to this remote part of Ireland to play golf in sufficient numbers to support and maintain the enterprise?'

'That will not be easy, but you have one thing in your favour: at Lahinch you have a course that is as good as any. Perhaps you should try running an open week with a big, all-comers championship included? If you can arrange that it take place the week before or after the Irish Open Amateur Championship, many of the players who come over from England and Scotland for that event might be persuaded to come early or to stay on to compete in both tournaments. Organize complimentary accommodation at the beginning as an incentive. I dare say that if you can get the players to come once, they will want to come back again, especially if you arrange the same hospitality that I have enjoyed while I have been here.

'Lahinch is like heaven on earth. I'll be sorry to leave it. If the village had a better class of accommodation and eating-house facilities, it would be a golfer's paradise. If I were you, I would think seriously about building a hotel close to the railway station. Watch the people come if you make it easy and comfortable for them to get here. The golf links and bathing beach will stand on their own merits.'

Alex Shaw listened intently. Within weeks he called an extraordinary meeting of the members of the golf club (no more than a dozen committed souls) and proposed that, as a group, they should underwrite the cost of building a hotel and that they should immediately organize a two-week jamboree of tournaments to attract people from far-flung places. Shaw, as usual, got his way.

In 1896, the Golf Links Hotel, a stunning example of nineteenth-century Norwegian-style luxury, was built. As one of its attractions it offered hot seawater baths. The seawater was pumped straight from the Atlantic, up and over the formidable cliff edge, to be discharged into every bedroom, having been heated on the way. The presence of the Golf Links Hotel underpinned the viability of Lahinch Golf Club and village for many years, but it did not open for business before another one of Old Tom's ideas, the South of Ireland Amateur Championship, was under way.

'The South', as it is now affectionately known, is the oldest provincial golf championship in Ireland and it reflects the way the social scene surrounding golf in Ireland has changed over the years. In 1895 golf balls cost 2 shillings each, which, hard to believe, was the same price being paid for a much better quality ball after the Second World War, fifty years later. Two shillings was also the price of a five-course meal in a top-class hotel. The relative wealth required to be able to play golf in 1895 would be beyond the capacity of most people today.

In 1927 Dr Alister Mackenzie, the architectural genius who designed Augusta and Cypress Point, was engaged to upgrade Morris's work. Mackenzie moved the six holes that were on the far side of the Liscannor Road into the dunes. Until then, exploiting the dunes was considered too costly an undertaking. Lahinch, these days, is very much a Mackenzie monument, having been extensively refurbished in that vein under the supervision of Martin Hawtree in 1999. Only one of Old Tom Morris's original holes remains intact today, the quirky Dell (5th). Although totally out of step with modern thinking, it would require a seismic adjustment in local attitudes for this last vestige of Old Tom's stay at Lahinch to be removed.

The first 'South', in 1895, was a gala affair. In attendance was the Chief Secretary of Ireland (in effect the Prime Minister), John Balfour, an excellent golfer who had been the Honorary Captain of the R&A the previous year and had also written one of the earliest classics of golfing literature, *Reminiscences of Golf at St Andrews Links* (1887). Political spin-doctoring existed as far back as the nineteenth century. The *Irish Times* reported that the Chief Secretary 'had gone to the country to be amongst the people to ascertain for himself what they think to be best for their welfare', when, in fact, you can be sure that he had really travelled down from Dublin to see for himself how good the golfing terrain might be.

The irony was, of course, that the Chief Secretary would not ascertain much about his subjects' welfare or otherwise at a golf meeting, as it was called back then. The ordinary Irish were peasants. They were in their fields tending to their animals and crops, blissfully unaware of the existence of the sport of golf and of Balfour's presence nearby. I am also quite sure that the people with whom he was associating at the golf club would have been horrified if it were thought that their welfare was in need of being assessed in any way.

In 1896, Alex Shaw placed an advertisement in the London *Times* offering overnight trips from Euston Station in London, via Liverpool and Dublin, by boat and train to Lahinch for the sum of 2 guineas each way. Shaw had persuaded the railway companies to arrange cheap excursion fares, subsidized by him, to attract golfers to come to Lahinch, just as the owners of hotels in Florida and the Carolinas were to do years later. The gimmick was a roaring success until the First World War intervened and the fortunes of the hotel began to dwindle. The Golf Links Hotel is long gone (its Norwegian wooden frame burnt to a cinder in 1937), but the South of Ireland Championship and Lahinch's seaside village with its thriving golf resort are more popular than ever.

But let us get back, if we may, to eavesdrop on one of Old Tom Morris and Sir Alex Shaw's fireside chats at Lahinch.

'Mr Shaw, sir, everybody knows the Scots invented, nurtured and refined the game of golf. So where, why and how did golf begin in Ireland?' asked Morris of Shaw one evening.

'Two of our own countrymen brought golf to the Ards Peninsula in Ulster in 1606,' Shaw began. 'On the death of Elizabeth I, Hugh Montgomery, the Laird of Braidstane, near Ayr, and Captain James Hamilton, both Scottish military adventurers, were rewarded for their loyalty to James VI of Scotland by being allowed to buy up huge tracts of land cheaply in the province of Ulster. King James was a golfing Stuart just like his mother, Mary, Queen of Scots. His two friends at Ards built a course for the King to play over when His Majesty made a royal excursion to Ulster shortly after his coronation.

'Subsequently the game appears to have suffered a hiatus, and may even have died out. In 1851, four hundred years after golf first began on the east coast of Scotland, another committed golf missionary migrated to Ireland. David Ritchie was the messiah who became the prime mover in the establishment of Ireland's first properly laid-out course at The Curragh in County Kildare. Ritchie wasted no time in getting things up and running in the correct manner, infecting a small, exclusive band of close associates with the golf bug in the process.'

Before going any further, it is important to point out that images of modern multi-million-dollar golf start-ups should be put clean out of our minds when imagining the way that the business of laying out a golf course was undertaken back then. The only requirements were to find a piece of under-used land and a man skilled in the wielding of a scythe. A mere 30 acres was considered sufficient to begin with and, of course, some basic knowledge of the game. Holes were rarely longer than 250 yards and new golf courses almost always consisted of six or nine holes at the start-up stage.

Back to Shaw's narrative. 'Another major part of the Irish jigsaw fell into place in 1852,' he said, 'when William Archibald Montgomerie, Earl of Eglinton, was appointed First Lord Lieutenant of Ireland. Eglinton was a founder member of the Prestwick Golf Club in Scotland and a most enthusiastic golfer. Monty, as he was affectionately known, was dedicated to the promotion of the game. Whenever he could get away from his duties at Dublin Castle, he would travel to The Curragh by horse-drawn coach to encourage Ritchie's endeavours. During his short political tenure in Ireland, Lord Eglinton became the fulcrum of the sudden surge of interest in golf by the Irish upper classes. This may have been down to their wish to keep up with the Joneses, so to speak, as much as to any genuine interest in a new activity that would provide them with healthy exercise and a pleasurable challenge.

'When Monty went back home to Scotland, he continued to play a major and historic part in the development of the game. As Lord Eglinton, he personally presented the Open Championship belt that was to be won outright by your late, lamented son, Young Tom Morris, in 1870.'

Tears welled up in Old Tom's eyes and he gave a big sigh.' Aye indeed. I often played with Monty at Prestwick and St Andrews, and gave him many a lesson. He was a dashing player. Och, I will never get over losing Young Tommy. Losing our son was as mortal a loss to the game of golf as it was to his grieving mother and me. Tommy would have set records that would never have been broken.'

Before Morris and Shaw shuffled away out of our ambit, Tail Gunner asked, 'Gentlemen, may I ask you were there any outstanding Irish golfers in your era?' Old Tom's eyes twinkled brightly; he obviously relished the question.

'You are going to be surprised by my answer, laddie. You must remember that at the turn of the twentieth century golf was still very much in its infancy in the United States. Therefore, by definition, the best golfers were all British. Whoever won any of the British Championships could rightly be considered the champion golfer and two young Irishwomen won the British Ladies' Championship five times between them in the nine-year spell from 1899 to 1907.

'In 1899 May Hezlet, a slip of a girl only seventeen years old and a supreme stylist, won the championship for the first of three times. To all intents and purposes that made her the champion woman golfer. She came from a family of outstanding golfers. Her mother Violet, brother Charles and sisters Florence and Emily were all champions. Every weekend, the family cycled a 24-mile round trip to get in a game of golf at Portrush. May was the best of them, sporting a domestic handicap of +7.

'Miss Hezlet was such a wonderful player that it is hard to believe that Rhona Adair from Killymoon may have been even better. Wee Rhona was also just seventeen when she won the Ladies' Championship in 1900. She won again in 1903 and also won the Irish Close four years running, from 1900 to 1903.

'In 1899, Miss Adair created quite a stir by bravely taking me on in an unheard of battle of the sexes over 36-holes at St Andrews. I was seventy-seven years old and Rhona only sixteen, but I had no wish to be licked by a lassie. Only one hole up at halfway, I dragged myself to a three-hole lead with nine holes to go, but then had to hold on for dear life as youthful stamina began to make a difference. In the end, I just managed to hang on by the skin of my teeth to win by a single hole. I got the fright of my life, especially when that wee girl out-drove me! Rhona Adair was renowned as a long-hitter and this ability more than anything else was the cause of her being invited to accompany the incomparable Harry Vardon on a wide-ranging tour of the United States and Canada in the autumn of 1903.'

In an article in *Irish Golfer* magazine, May Hezlet wrote about her friend as follows:

> Rhona's USA trip was a wonderful success. She carried off sixteen trophies from the different courses she visited. Only once during the time she was there was she defeated by an American lady golfer and when it is taken into consideration that she was in a strange land and climate and playing on unfamiliar turf, after a great deal of travelling and rushing about, her success appears something marvellous. No other lady in the world could have performed such wonders or given the American people such a splendid exhibition. The visit made a tremendous sensation and will probably arouse fresh interest in the game of golf, enlisting many new members into the growing ranks of enthusiasts in the United States.

The famous British player, Harold Hilton, said of Rhona:

> She stands up to the ball in a manner quite worthy of the sterner sex. There is determination and firmness in her address. Lady golfers as a general rule appear to persuade the ball on its way; Miss Adair, on the contrary, hits very hard indeed.

Tom Morris concluded, 'Rhona's power play was unique and it astonished her American hosts. She was undoubtedly the best Irish golfer I ever saw during my lifetime.'

Old Tom turned and spotted Arnold Haultain inspecting a wild flower in the distance.

'Look Mr Shaw, there's Professor Haultain. Let's go over and ask him how many species of wild orchid he has found on this fine new links. Adieu gentlemen. Perhaps we will meet again? Enjoy the rest of your game.'

For a minute, Tail Gunner and I watched the departing Old Tom and Sir Alex in stunned amazement, little realizing that an equally momentous adventure awaited us around the corner at the 12th tee.

6

The Mackenzieization of Lahinch

W HEN BOB JONES beckoned me on to the beach beyond the 13th green at Doonbeg, I was fearful that if I joined him my mortal existence would be at an end. Suffice to say I was not quite ready for that journey into the unknown, even though it appeared that I had nothing to worry about concerning the quality of golf available in the after-life.

While I may have taken full advantage of a chance meeting with Bob Jones, I would like to remind you that it was he who had introduced himself into my orbit, not the other way round. How was I to know he would be standing on the 12th tee at Doonbeg, waiting for Tail Gunner and me to come along?

'Can I play along with y'all?' Jones had asked.

Surely posing questions to a ghost was not a mortal sin? If it was good enough for Tail Gunner, it was also good enough for me.

James Carew may have played only two holes of golf with Robert Tyre Jones Junior but already they seemed to have built a strong rapport. The rapid formation of friendship is frequently one of the best side-effects of playing golf. I was well aware that Tail Gunner was the kind of guy that Jones would have been more than happy to have as a member of Augusta National. As well as being a scratch golfer, he was good company, knowledgeable on many subjects, witty, wise and discreet. His dry humour, debating skills and thoughtfulness would have contributed enormously to the institutions and traditions of the game at the highest levels if the opportunity had ever arisen.

'The timing of your eventual crossing over is not Bob Jones's department, nor mine either,' said Tail Gunner, dismissing my fears. 'Bob merely wants us to join him for purely golfing reasons. So hurry up! I want to know what he has up his sleeve, even if you don't!'

Taken by the elbow, I was led gently through a gap in the dunes at the edge of the golf course, where, to my astonishment, instead of Doughmore Beach we found ourselves stepping on to the familiar territory of Little Island, the home ground of Cork Golf Club.

Jones was standing in the centre of the 4th tee, which backs into the Lee Estuary, leaning on his driver, head bowed slightly while he listened resignedly to an agitated gentleman who was lecturing him severely. As we drew closer, the animated one's impressive moustache, flashing dark eyes and highly bronzed features became vaguely familiar. A third gentleman, whom I knew I had never set eyes upon before, was standing with his back to the conversation, calmly smoking a pipe and observing a rust-laden tugboat chugging up the river towards the city.

The figure watching the boat was not dressed for golf. He wore baggy, loose-fitting corduroy trousers held up by garish braces. The sleeves of his rough, collarless cotton shirt were rolled up past his elbows; he looked out of place, more like a labourer than a golfer. I wondered what he was doing in such company. Noticing our arrival, Jones halted the verbal barrage with a wave of his hand and formally introduced us.

'This is Dr Alister Mackenzie, of whom y'all will of course have heard, and one of his closest colleagues in his course-construction enterprise, Jack Fleming.'

Having already had a preview of what might have been upsetting Mackenzie, Tail Gunner and I had no wish to be dragged into the affair. We withdrew to talk to Mr Fleming. What an eye-opener that turned out to be! Without much prompting, Fleming proceeded to recount a shorthand version of his life story.

'I was born and reared in Tuam, County Galway. I left in 1916 at the age of twenty and went to England in search of a formal qualification in horticulture. After graduating with my diploma from Manchester Polytechnic Institute, I was fully intent on finding a position in a large estate or commercial nursery somewhere in England. I couldn't find the kind of employment I sought, which turned out to be rather fortunate. Completely by chance, and almost as a last resort, I found work as a labourer with the British Golf Course Construction Company, which was independently operated by Major Charles A. Mackenzie to exploit his famous golf-course architect brother's growing fame. At the outset, my attitude to working for the Mackenzies was that it would help keep body and soul together until something better turned up.

'By 1920, I had graduated from the labouring ranks to the position of site foreman. I had a flair for landscaping and growing good-quality grass. I was able to interpret Alister's scribbled notes and rough drawings better than his brother was. To be honest, I used to tone down many of Mac's more radical ideas when it actually came to moving earth around, and as he rarely saw his courses after construction, he never found out. Gradually, I grew to understand the golf-course design and construction business inside out. Then, in 1927, I came back to Ireland with Mac to supervize several projects that he had undertaken here. We did not know it at the time, but it was to be the beginning of the sudden and dramatic explosion in Mac's international reputation. What he achieved at Lahinch especially was the springboard to the winning of valuable contracts in the United States and Australia that would in due course become his legacy.

'The pattern was nearly always the same. We would arrive early in the morning and march briskly over the land. As we went along, Mac would talk incessantly. I took all my notes mentally while he scribbled feverishly. By lunchtime Mac would have a pretty good idea of the general routing. He had incredible energy and a sharp eye for detail. He was quite capable of staying up all night with a bottle of whisky, sketching. He also had the uncanny knack of getting things right first pop. Most of all he was a marvellous salesman of his own ideas. Weird sketches and a torrent of words bamboozled promoters who had nothing to go on except topographical maps. To them Mac's way of doing things must have been highly mysterious.

'When Mac and I went to Lahinch in 1927, it was already one of the best-known and respected courses in the British Isles. The South of Ireland Amateur Championship had been up and running since 1895 and the course had a major reputation in England and Scotland. Many of the top players in that era, including the likes of Harold Hilton from Hoylake, made an annual pilgrimage across the Irish Sea. A few of them, though surprisingly not Hilton, were successful. The links that Old Tom Morris laid out in 1894 had been further revised by Charles Gibson in 1910. Lahinch was Mac's biggest challenge to date and he was acutely aware of it. He made sure of putting his best foot forward by spending twice as long as usual studying the layout – i.e. two days – before putting pen to paper.

'At the time, six (Tom Morris) holes were situated across the road. Mackenzie's brief was to shift all the holes across Liscannor Road to the ocean side and to build some new holes amongst the unexploited virgin dunes along the shoreline.

'Once Mac had his ideas and drawings approved and the deal was signed and sealed, he took off in search of the next project, leaving me in charge as clerk of works and construction foreman. I did all the purchasing of materials as well as the hiring and firing. At the same time as the work was taking place at Lahinch, we came here to Little Island too. There were also less ambitious projects at Monkstown, Muskerry, Douglas and Limerick to be taken care of at the same time.

'At Lahinch, we were lucky to recruit a particularly able local lieutenant in Willie McCavery from County Down. Willie had only just been appointed club professional at Lahinch. In those days it was normal that the club pro would not only be a club-

maker and teacher, but he would also take on the duties of head
greens superintendent as well. McCavery was utterly dependable
and went on to stay in this capacity at Lahinch for over fifty
years, becoming famous all over the world as a supreme crafts-
man in wooden club-making. In the halcyon days of persimmon,
a McCavery driver was a much sought-after piece of equipment.

'Like a juggler, I moved back and forth between all the loca-
tions. As Mac rarely revisited a site once his plans had been
accepted, he did not realize that inevitable minor alterations to
his plans took place. He was such a stickler for detail that if he
had ever found out that we had done something that was not to
his liking he would have eaten us for breakfast.

'All this work in Ireland took a full year to complete. Then I was
invited to follow Mac to California, where he had a number of
exciting projects in the pipeline. Cypress Point was one of them.

'The stock market crash of 1929 badly affected the golf-
course construction business. By 1932 business was at a complete halt. On Mac's advice, and with much sadness, I left his
firm and became the Director of Public Parks in San Francisco. It
was a job that suited me ideally. One of my responsibilities was
to oversee the building of several municipal golf courses in northern California, possibly the most famous of them being Harding
Park where I now have the honour of one of the nines being
named after me.

'I continued to dabble in golf-course architecture as a sideline
until my retirement in 1962, designing and building twenty golf
courses around the Bay area of San Francisco. My healthy, out-
door lifestyle ensured that I lived until the ripe old age of ninety-
one. My son, John, followed in my footsteps to a certain extent
by holding the prestige post of head greens superintendent at the
Olympic Club in San Francisco for many years.'

Hearing all this for the first time, I could not help thinking
that, while Mackenzie may have been the creative genius who
made the sales pitch and drew up the routing plan, it was Jack
Fleming who shaped the earth, made vital on-the-spot decisions

and final alterations. Fleming had obviously done the lion's share of the work on many of Mackenzie's famous golf courses without receiving any of the notoriety or glory. Mackenzie may have been the entrepreneur, but Fleming saw to it that the ideas became a reality. I was stunned to learn that a humble Irishman from County Galway was so vital to the Mackenzie legacy.

After a few gentle sucks at his pipe, Fleming began speaking again.

'I am very fond of Cork Golf Club because this is where I got my first big break and where I was put in sole charge for the first time. After only two days and one night plotting the routing, Mac literally handed me his plans and departed for California on a new prospecting mission. It was my sole responsibility, without the assistance of daily telephone conversations, texts or faxes, to oversee all of the site works. I had to plan the *modus operandi*, calculate the bills of quantities and budgets, pay the wages, while making sure that the job was done in an exemplary manner. From day one, Cork Golf Club was a lovely location with attractive terrain. It has matured magnificently and, apart from the run of holes down by the river, it is barely recognizable. So many trees! To be fair, the changes that have been made by the members over the years are normal evolution and have not taken from the original concept.'

While Jack Fleming was telling us his story, we watched Bob Jones break off from having his ears singed to hit another silky smooth drive over the elbow of the rocky estuary. Tail Gunner took his customary safe line, his golf ball skipping along the springy turf until it reached a small rise in the fairway 225 yards from the tee. Mackenzie's swing was quick and jerky. His badly sliced shot never had a chance of clearing the shoreline, but came down on the rocks, where it bounced around erratically for a moment or two before disappearing into a watery grave. An unintelligible Scottish oath was uttered before he replayed. This time his ball snap-hooked over a bush, almost beheading Tony Finn and Dennis Clifford, a pair of members who were standing on the 11th tee waiting for the fairway ahead to clear.

Bob signalled for Fleming to play next, but he declined. 'I'd prefer to absorb the atmosphere if you don't mind,' he said in his soft west of Ireland accent.

When it was my turn to play, I pushed my tee-shot slightly but was relieved to see it just clear the water and find the edge of the fairway, giving me an undeserved advantage of opening up the entrance to the narrow green tantalizingly placed on a gentle rise of ground 200 yards away.

After some thrashing around in the heather, a disgruntled Mac found his ball. There was no immediate improvement on the horizon, as he eventually holed out in nine of the untidiest strokes I have ever seen by man or ghost. With varying degrees of difficulty and ease, Tail Gunner, Jones and I all managed to secure par 4s. Being the first to exit the green, I walked briskly towards the shore where the 5th tee is located.

'Where are you going? The next tee is not over there!' Mackenzie roared after me, allowing the irritation caused by his bad play to get the better of him.

'Wait until you see what has been done over here, Dr Mackenzie,' I called over my shoulder. 'Don't you think it is always a good idea to get as close to the water's edge as one can?'

When Mac saw the way in which 'his' 5th hole had been altered, he grudgingly approved. As we walked down the shore-line and got closer to the green that juts into the estuary, his mood began to thaw and he actually became complimentary.

After scoring another perfectly played par, Bob Jones said, 'If it is spectacular golf holes near water you want, gentlemen, let's pop down the coast to Old Head Links!'

In a flash we were deposited a few miles away on the stunning 12th tee at the Old Head Links, built on a narrow neck of rocky headland jutting defiantly into the Atlantic, 300 feet above the sea. Anyone who suffers from vertigo should stay well clear. The cliffs on all sides are sheer and the carries from tee to fairway are intimidating and terrifying.

'The 12th hole at Old Head is one of the wonders of the golf world,' Bob Jones began. 'No matter how far one travels, or how much it might cost, any golfer worth his salt has to experience this extraordinary place at least once in his lifetime.'

Jones's infectious chuckle broke out once again as he lashed yet another glorious drive daringly over a small white stone marker that was much too close to the cliff edge for my comfort.

'A large helping of intestinal fortitude is essential to bring off shots like that, because who is to know if there is a fairway up there?' laughed Tail Gunner, catching Jones's mood.

Walking along the track between tee and fairway I felt the need to be distracted from the no-man's land on my left, and the fall to certain death if one lost one's footing, by seizing upon the opportunity to speak directly to Mackenzie.

'I understand your friends call you Mac. Is it okay if I do likewise?'

'Och, of course, Golf Nut.'

Under no illusion that the answers I might receive would be to my liking, I pressed ahead.

'Have you, by any chance, seen the so-called Mackenzieization of Lahinch by Hawtree and Company?' I asked.

Mac's dark eyebrows furrowed and his moustache twitched. 'Aye, I have indeed, and I must say it is a bit of a curate's egg: good in spots!'

'What do you mean, Mac?'

'Aesthetically I cannot criticize what the third generation of the Hawtree firm of golf architects has done in my name at Lahinch. But would you please tell them that conceiving a golf course from the standpoint of exclusively rewarding expert play to the detriment of ninety-eight per cent of golfers is incorrect.'

'Don't speak to me in riddles, Mac – tell me straight. What exactly do you mean?'

'A golf course should be playable by every standard of golfer. Lahinch is not,' he said tersely. There was a short pause as he made a half-hearted attempt to get away from me, but he was unable to contain himself. He stopped walking, turned to face me and let rip.

'As I see it, Lahinch has become too severe and penal. Too many of the carries from tee to fairway are beyond the capacity of most players. There is too much high grass near the fairways and greens. There are not enough bail-out areas. Since when has the greens being wider than the fairways running into them become fashionable? The aprons are so bumpy in places that running an approach on to the putting surfaces with any degree of certainty is no longer an option. On a links that is exposed to high winds from the ocean, ground golf should be catered for; target golf is never compatible with fast-running seaside turf.'

'Back in 1927, what was your own approach to the task?' I asked tentatively.

'My original aim was to create a course that would be a beautiful picture and could be enjoyed equally by tigers and rabbits. Hawtree has certainly added to the beauty by moulding new holes overlooking the beach – those were outside my budget – but he seems to have forgotten that the majority of golfers are rabbits and do not hit the ball far enough, or with sufficient control, to be able to play such a difficult golf course. Personally, I never came close to the lofty standard of being a scratch player, nor do ninety-eight per cent of golfers. You should not build a golf course to test scratch golfers at the expense of high handicappers.

'By all means make a course look hard, but it should actually play easy if one uses one's brains. When the wind blows hard at Lahinch, it is impossible for the majority of golfers to get round without losing three or four golf balls. At €5 a go, where is the fun in that? Too much impenetrable rough close to the playing area gobbles up golf balls and slows play to a crawl. If the grass were cut, all the humps, hollows, bunkers and mounding would make the game difficult enough.'

'What about the severe undulations on the greens? Would you agree that some are overdone?' I asked.

'Absolutely! The 16th is one green that can give a pretty decent shot short shrift. Nor is there a safe area at the expense of half a shot, or even one shot, to counteract a potential disaster,' replied Mac, who was now well and truly established on his soap-box. 'My cardinal rules of good golf-course architecture are well documented but apparently forgotten. I think I had better repeat some of them here and now.'

'Oh no! This is going to be worse than one of those damn blow-by-blows!' exclaimed Jones, feigning shock and horror.

Mackenzie saw the humour and laughed, but it did not prevent him from launching into a blistering litany.

'Every golf course should be an examination of skill rather than muscle; an interesting and stimulating challenge for the scratch player while also being playable for high-handicappers. The time-wasting, irritation and annoyance of searching for lost golf balls in high grass should be totally eliminated from the game. There should be a minimum of blindness on approach shots. Fairways and greens should be undulating, but there should be minimal hill-climbing. There should be a large proportion of strong two-shot holes, two or three drive-and-pitch holes, and at least four one-shot holes of varying lengths and directions. Every hole should have a different character. There should be little walking between greens and tees, and the course should be laid out in two distinct loops of nine holes. Shall I go on?'

Nobody had the nerve to stop him now.

'There should be a number of heroic carries from the back tees, but there should also be forward tees for the older, weaker players, who, with the loss of stroke or maybe a portion of a stroke, will have an alternative route open to them.'

'Touché! I did not see many alternative routes at Lahinch,' exclaimed Jones, who had been eavesdropping avidly. He went on, 'Length has very little to do with the quality of a golf hole. It should be a matter of getting the correct angle of approach and controlling the distance one hits the ball. The King of Lahinch, John Burke, told me that once upon a time Lahinch was arguably the best course in Ireland in the wideness of its appeal to golfers of all standards. Now, he feared that it has been made overly difficult and would not be enjoyed by the average player as much as it once was.'

'Don't be too hard on the architect!' Fleming interjected. 'In our day we did not have to contend with balls that fly like bullets for up to 350 yards down breeze without the complications of side-spin. In the twenty-first century, the game has become primarily one of power. Imagination and inventiveness are not as much a part of the test as they once were.'

Before another row broke out, this time between Mac and his Irish foreman, Jones announced that he was going to take us to Africa.

7

The Future is Africa!

BEFORE ONE COULD SAY 'Papwa Sewgolum',* Jones, Mac, Fleming, Tail Gunner and yours truly were spirited away to the western Cape on the southernmost tip of Africa, where we found ourselves standing on one of the most beautiful stretches of cliff-top coastline imaginable.

A beaming Bob Jones pointed theatrically in the direction of a burly, rugby-player type, who made the ground shudder underneath us when he jumped from a power cart, which had screeched to a halt nearby only moments earlier. As the driver lumbered towards us in the manner of the menacing open-side flanker that he once was, Darren Clarke was instantly recognizable.

'Welcome to Pinnacle Point, golf course of the future, designed by one of my favourite Irishmen, Big D'arn!' Jones announced, grinning from ear to ear.

On first sight, Clarke's cliff-top course overlooking the Indian Ocean closely resembled Lahinch and Ballybunion in the 1960s, before watering systems were heard of in Ireland – i.e. tawny brown and running fast. The emerald green of Africa may not have been as vivid and the brown had a distinct reddish hue, but otherwise the course looked surprisingly similar to those that Tail Gunner and I had played as teenagers.

* Of Indian extraction, Papwa Sewgolum was a victim of the Apartheid regime in South Africa, which prevented him from competing as a professional golfer in his homeland. For a short spell during the 1960s, Papwa was a popular and successful member of the European Tour.

'Why is the golf course so burnt up? Have you no irrigation?' Tail Gunner asked sternly.

'One of the biggest issues in third millennium golf is water conservation. It has become increasingly difficult to find sufficient water to maintain golf courses. I don't worry too much about it, because golfers should be able to adjust to whatever conditions are thrown at them. It's the essence of the game that, no matter what the conditions are, there will always be winners and losers. From the beginning, golf was intended to be a ground game as much as an in-the-air game. A complete golfer will exert control over the ball's bounce and roll as well as its trajectory and flight. As the twenty-first century unfolded, the imagination and skill required for a full artillery of bump-and-run ground strokes as well as flighted shapes was close to being lost to the game for ever,' said Darren Clarke in his soft Dungannon lilt.

'Why do you say that?' asked Mac.

'When I was in my prime, too many courses were so soft that golf was like playing darts on grass,' answered Darren.

Tail Gunner had this to say: 'If you ask me, golf began to lose its soul at the same time. So much wealth was being generated that the ruling bodies became rich beyond their wildest dreams. Instead of doing the job that they were supposed to do – caring for the ethos of the game – they became more concerned about protecting their investments and growing their financial portfolios. By failing to limit and control the huge technological advances, top players were allowed to hit the ball distances never imagined by the architects of earlier eras. Virtually overnight, our great traditional courses became obsolete. New technology was developing so fast that even brand-new courses could not cope. In their greed for profit, equipment manufacturers showed scant respect for the well-being of the game. Golfers were treated as consumers instead of as enthusiasts who loved a challenge. Every six-months or so a new ball or driver that would achieve another 20 yards was launched. The public was mesmerized by so many marketers appealing to its vanity. The prospect of purchasing the

power to hit the ball a long way, without going through the drudg-
ery and discipline of hard work on the practice ground or in the
gym, was irresistible.

'The irony was that while unremitting power was allowed to
go unfettered, the game became more difficult for novices who
could not manage drastically lengthened golf courses, but it was
easier for the pros who had the talent to exploit the new equipment to the ultimate degree. Golf architects were at their wits'
end as new courses were pronounced too short and out of date
no sooner than they had opened for play. The amount of expensive land required to build challenging and safe golf courses esca-
lated beyond affordability.'

'What year is this?' I asked, becoming alarmed.

Before Tail Gunner could continue, Darren replied, 'It's 2022.
I retired from tournament golf twelve years ago to concentrate
exclusively on taking care of my family and my growing golf
property and design business. Building new golf courses and re-
inventing old ones is more satisfying than travelling the globe
week in, week out. I was tired of starting every tournament week
with nothing and hoping that by the end of it there would be a
pay cheque. Being with my family and seeing them happy and
fulfilled is all that matters to me. I have invested millions in
Africa, but it has been a wise move. Pinnacle Point is only the
first of several projects on this stretch of coastline to be designed
and built by Darren Clarke International Golf Properties. When
I originally moved down to the Cape, for what I thought would
be a six-month spell, I had no idea that I would still be here
twelve years later. Golf has been one of the main driving forces
behind the tourism boom in South Africa, attracting enormous
foreign investment.

'Not everyone can play the game to a high standard, so it is
important that golf takes place in attractive and memorable surroundings. The joy of being free to wander around in a beautiful
location with the occasional sighting of a wild animal cannot be
overestimated. I was what you might call an inspirational, flair

player rather than a methodical grinder and I try to reflect that type of attitude in my course designs.

'Pinnacle Point is halfway between Port Elizabeth and Cape Town. Thirty years ago this was a hundred miles of uninhabited wilderness, but the potential was instantly recognizable. It's my own piece of heaven. I especially like the idea that my golf courses will be around long after I have shuffled off this mortal coil.' As he spoke, Clarke lit up two enormous cigars and handed one of them to Bob.

Tail Gunner resumed: 'Until the 1980s it was possible to play eighteen holes in less than three hours, the player rather than his equipment dictating the results. The constant lengthening of courses, plus the continuing rise in the cost of land, became ruinous. A war of attrition with the manufacturers, who cared only about their bottom lines and little about the purity of the game, broke out before the game's legislators finally found the courage to limit technology.'

I joined in, saying, 'That's right! It amazes me that in my sixties I can hit longer and more accurate driver shots that I could ever manage in my prime. Only when manufacturers were finally forced to slow down the initial velocity of the ball coming off the club-face to a base Y2K standard was the game saved. By reducing the number of clubs allowed in top tournaments from fourteen to ten, imagination and inventiveness were also brought back into vogue. After a short era of golf courses being overpowered by super-fit athletes, shot-making skills and tactics became the primary means of achieving success once again.'

'By Jove, we foresaw all that happening in 1927, didn't we Bob?' exclaimed Mackenzie. 'I can remember you suggesting to the USGA that a tournament ball with speed governors should be adopted. You wrote that the length of classic courses should be pegged at 6,300 yards and that a 7,000-yard golf course would make the game too difficult and too slow for average players. All other sports that I can think of have standard tournament balls. Why not golf?'

Jones's carefree spirit seemed to have evaporated temporarily as he joined in: 'In my day, I was one of the longer hitters, often reaching 280 yards, but people forget 50 or 60 yards of that was roll. When irrigation systems were installed on fairways, that much roll became impossible. The idea of carrying the ball over 350 yards is mind-boggling. It should not have taken the legislators so long to appreciate that creative approach play, short-game wizardry and heroic recovery play were more fun for everybody, players and fans included.'

Then Jack Fleming spoke. 'When amateurs could no longer relate to the game that the pros played, they began to lose interest in watching them. Besides, golf has always been more of a participator sport, with recreational players more interested in playing their own game than watching others, no matter how skilled they might be. Without large numbers of spectators, professional golf began to die. However, you will be glad to hear that in the year 2022 the game has returned to the way it was intended to be: 400 yards is a challenging par 4; 500 yards is a genuine three-shotter. The adoption of a slower, lighter, slightly larger tournament ball for the Masters Tournament at Augusta in 2009 was the catalyst for change. One sad development was that Tiger Woods, who possessed more creative skill and inventiveness than anybody in the history of the game, did not wait around to show us how he might have coped. He retired prematurely from competition two wins short of Jack Nicklaus's major tournament wins record. Some say Tiger objected to the curtailing of the ball's speed. He, publicly at least, made the argument that progress should be allowed to flourish without restrictions. Privately, he may have felt differently. I believe that Tiger was worn down by invasions of his privacy. He turned his back on the game in his early thirties to live the life of a hermit aboard a seafaring boat in the Caribbean with his Swedish wife and fifteen (twelve of them adopted) children.

'As I remember it, the range at which somebody could be in danger of getting clobbered by a loose golf ball had become too wide. The enormous distances the ball carried through the air, even when struck by a novice, had to be curtailed. When ball velocity and the distance travelled became serious health and safety issues, the legislators were finally forced to make changes. Manufacturers came under pressure for selling lethal weapons to unlicensed idiots who could not control their products. In that atmosphere, manufacturers were finally persuaded to relent. Balls with self-correcting aerodynamic dimpling were outlawed too. The creative swerve shot that had been eliminated from the game was brought back.'

Tail Gunner changed the tone of the conversation by asking, 'Pinnacle Point looks a fine course, Darren. What is the total yardage and when did you open for play?'

'In 2006 and 6,831 from the tips. If the golf ball had been allowed to continue developing without any checks, this course would have to be close to 8,500 yards. That is too far to walk in a hot afternoon. With the obligatory pit stops, it would have taken six hours. Wisdom prevailed, fortunately.'

Bob Jones was becoming restless, impatient to be on the move again. 'I'd appreciate it if y'all would come with me on a short trip down the coast. I want y'all to meet somebody real special. I think y'all might like to tag along with us too, Darren.'

Before we could shout 'Fore!', we were transported to Pearl Valley, a twenty-year-old Jack Nicklaus creation. I began telling Tail Gunner how he had missed out on the only time that the Golden Bear (Nicklaus) had come to Ireland to compete in a major championship. Nicklaus had played golf privately in Ireland on numerous occasions, but only once did he put his tournament face on, at Royal County Down in the 2001 British Seniors Open.

As I savoured the memory, a sprightly eighty-two-year-old Jack Nicklaus emerged from behind a dusty pick-up truck. Dressed in a long-sleeved plaid work shirt, faded jeans, muddy construction boots and battered golf cap, none of us recognized him at first. He appeared to have shrunk alarmingly with age, but he still displayed a formidable aura. His clear blue eyes sparkled with good humour and determination.

'Sorry I'm late boys, I was on a cat skinner trying to knock the side of that fairway trap on no. 7 into shape!' he said cheerily, perspiring profusely from the heat and exertion. 'When I heard that you fellows were here, I had to drop everything and go search for that damn pen belonging to the Golf Nut that I've had since Augusta '81. I was pretty sore with myself for three-stabbing the 18th green and handing the initiative to Watson going into the final eighteen. The Golf Nut cornered me in the clubhouse saying he would like an autograph for his wife, goddammit! He began barraging me with the same damn questions that I had answered in the media centre only minutes earlier. My patience was all used up. I could not get away quickly enough and I inadvertently took his pen. I did come back to return it a few minutes later when I realized my mistake, but there you were, gone!'

Then, smiling broadly and looking me straight in the eye, he said in his surprisingly high-pitched voice, 'It's a nice pen, but my wife Barbara always said that you would show up one day looking for it!'

'Not at all, Jack – I was amused and flattered that you had purloined my pen,' I replied with a wide grin.

On seeing that Nicklaus was in high spirits, Darren Clarke thought that he might take the opportunity to ask him a few questions.

'What are you doing in Africa at your age? You should be at home in Florida with your feet up!'

'Nah! I'll keep going as hard as I can until I drop. At this stage, I've been building golf courses for longer than I was winning championships, and I must tell you that building them in Africa is the most fun. Forget that 17-mile drive in California; this part of South Africa has a hundred miles of coastline littered with fine golf courses. I've built eighteen of them. The wee man [Gary Player] has built even more.'

Becoming serious, Darren asked, 'Jack, you have the best record of anyone in golf history. You have always been admired for the way you have handled yourself as much as for your many victories. How did you manage to do it? What was your secret?'

'I have no idea! From an early age, winning golf tournaments is what I did best in life. I had tremendous support from those around me, especially my dad and my mentor since boyhood, Jack Grout. I simply gave every day my best shot and it worked out. All I did was study the golf course, prepare a plan, stick to it and hope for the best. I concentrated on playing my own game and allowing the others to take themselves out of contention, which most of them did most of the time.'

Then they were off. There was no stopping Darren and Jack as they went on their own private head-to-head of reminiscing.

'Is Royal County Down the best course that you've played in Ireland?'

'Couldn't really say. I haven't played enough of them,' said Jack. 'All those blind shots, weird tilts to the fairways and greens, and unpredictable bounces kind of got on my nerves a little bit, especially in the windy conditions. But you don't change a golf course that is 150 years old. Old Tom Morris would not be pleased if anyone interfered with his layout. We should accept it as it is. I've never been shy to criticize a golf course if I felt it was deserved, but I would be slow to make changes to Royal County Down, flawed though it may be.'

'What is your happiest golfing memory?' asked Tail Gunner, once again steering us away from controversy.

'I look forward to tomorrow and what that might bring far more than I look back on the past. I think only of what I want to do next. It's more fun to look forward than to look back on one's life, waiting for it to be over.'

Darren grew more confident in his questioning. 'Jack, you had the ability to be objective coming down the finishing straight. Being able to leave emotion to one side and make cold calculating decisions really helped you. How did you manage to do it?'

'How do you know how I felt? Of course I felt emotion. If I hadn't got the buzz that I did from competing, I wouldn't have played. There's nothing better than being in the hunt and nothing worse than being out of it.'

'What is it about pressure golf that you liked best?' I butted in.

Without pausing, Jack answered, 'I liked to hit good golf shots when I had to. There is golf, and there is tournament golf, and the two are entirely different. Is that not correct, Mr Jones?'

'Damn right!' said Bob smiling, and then the elegant Georgian asked, 'You were an all-round sports jock, excelling at several sports during your high-school years. What makes golf different in your eyes?'

'Golf requires more confidence and self-reliance. You are on your own. Nobody can hit that ball for you, protect you or run interference for you.'

'What do you miss most about competitive golf?' asked Tail Gunner.

'I miss having to motivate myself to get the job done.'

'And what do you think is your legacy?' Darren asked.

'Arnold [Palmer] and I changed the way the game was played. We changed a game of style and finesse to one of power. For a generation or two all players played the power game. If they didn't, they had no chance. Arnold started the ball rolling in that direction, then I waded in full bore. We took the game in a different direction and everyone – players, equipment manufacturers, course builders and rules-makers – was forced to follow, whether they wanted to or not. Unfortunately, it all went a bit too far and technology equalized the advantage that Arnie and I once had from our natural ability.'

'So it was all your fault then?' asked Darren with a broad smile.

'Yeah, in a way, but the manufacturers took things too far and the separation between the great strikers and merely good ones became blurred. There was a skewed dividend for players who could get their swing speed above 120 mph. They could hit the ball a disproportionate distance to the guy who managed only 115 mph.'

Nicklaus was a revelation. I had rarely heard such an honest, matter-of-fact self-assessment, so upfront and free of false modesty. I decided to throw in a few more questions while I had the chance.

'You've already mentioned the confidence factor as being vital to success. Is it critical in separating the winners from the losers?' My question was directed at Nicklaus, but Jones answered.

'Champions need to be very self-possessed and self-assured. They need to be independent thinkers with the rare ability to remain focused on their own desires and goals no matter what is going on around them. They have to be emotionally selfish; not everybody can do that. A positive, objective outlook on one's own performance is essential, with the ability to be a pragmatic problem-solver when it comes to getting the job done. Golf is more than just a test of athletic ability. It is a test of judgement, patience, nerves and good decision-making under fire.'

'Well said, Bob! I can't improve on that!' laughed Jack.

Mackenzie was itching to be on the move again. 'Where to next, Bob?'

'You decide, Mac.'

'Okay. Let's go home to Pasatiempo!'

No sooner had we said our goodbyes to Darren and Jack, who were glad to go back to reshaping African soil, than we were looking down at a tee-marker that read 'PASATIEMPO, NO. 16. 385 YARDS. PAR 4'.

I felt bewildered. 'Pasatiempo? What part of the world are we in now?'

'Southern California. That I chose to live the last five years of my life on the Pasatiempo golf course had much to do with the fact that I could play early-morning golf in my pyjamas,' said Mac with a tear in his eye.

'Okay Mac, we will concede the honour to you,' Jones said, anxious to keep moving along.

Although only 385 yards long, it was obvious that the hole we were about to tackle was going to be no pushover. The tee-shot had to be played over a diagonal, dried-out barranca (gorge) before the fairway ran gently downhill through a funnel of cypress trees that crowded in on the right-hand side of the narrow landing area. The barranca continued along the left-hand side of the fairway before turning sharply to the right, crossing in front of the putting surface and running along the right-hand side of the green 10 feet below it.

'Mac's use of the barranca is brilliant!' exclaimed Jones. 'It has to be crossed no less than eight times during a round and on each occasion the task is slightly different.'

Even from the tee I could see that the putting surface was long and narrow. It had three ledges with distinctive tiers. Foolishly thinking about how I might manage such a difficult green, I pull-hooked straight into the barranca and lost my golf ball. Tail Gunner found the perfect spot on the fairway, but his second shot missed the green by 6 inches and tumbled in stop-start slow motion to the bottom of the ravine. Mac tick-tacked all over the lot. None of us finished the hole. Jones? Drive straight down the middle; then a silky smooth putt converted a laser-like mashie stroke into another birdie.

'If you don't mind, Bob, we made a mistake by coming here. It is too emotional for me here. We should have gone to Cypress Point, the 13th to be precise,' said a flustered Mac.

'The 13th?' an astonished Fleming intervened. 'What about the 16th? I thought that everybody wanted to play the 16th at Cypress.'

'The 13th appeals to me more,' replied Mac. 'That beautiful downhill drive with the Pacific Ocean as a heart-stopping backdrop gets my vote every time. I love driving over that diagonal series of low scrubby dunes that challenge and reward the brave player. By taking on the bigger carry on the right and going as close to the trouble as one dares, the next shot becomes proportionately easier. Going down the left-hand side is for the faint-hearted and makes the approach into the green more difficult. Play this hole aggressively and it will yield birdies; play it timidly and it will exert a price.

'When my colleagues Seth Raynor, Marion Hollins and I were planning the course, we debated for ages about whether the 16th should be a short par 4 or long par 3. One afternoon we were enjoying a picnic near where the tee box was eventually located. Seth looked wistfully across the cove and said that it was a shame that the carry was about 10 yards too long for us to make the best par 3 in the world. Marion sprang to her feet, grabbed a driver, teed up a ball, shifted her girdle and drove straight across the water on to the promontory where the green sits today.

'"There you are boys!" she declared triumphantly. "Case closed. If an old doll can make the carry, surely you guys can do it too?"' Mac chuckled. 'Of course, as a former US Women's Amateur Champion, Marion was a much better golfer than most men, but she sold me on the idea right there and then.'

'What about the awful 18th?' said Jones, with uncharacteristic bluntness.

'On almost every golf course,' Mac responded, 'the designer is at some stage forced to find a way to get from one impressive feature to another by mundane means. In Cypress Point's case it just happens that the 18th is the link. After building those fabulous seaside holes we had to face up to the anticlimax of bringing everybody back to the clubhouse by the most direct route possible. In the 1920s, the majority of club golf was match play. It is the nature of match play that most games between members would end before the 18th was reached. Therefore, nobody gave a hoot. If you are going to have a weak hole it might as well be the 18th, when fellows are tired, anxious to finish and looking forward to the comforts of the 19th. Now if you don't mind, Bob, would you please utter those magic words of yours and take us to New South Wales Golf Club down under in Australia?'

8

Down Under with Mac

E VER SINCE I WATCHED Peter Thomson and Gary Player battling the course and elements at Royal Melbourne in a mid-1960s filmed *Shell's Wonderful World of Golf* match, I have been an admirer of golf down under. Those fast-running fairways, pristine white sand traps and quick as lightening greens excited me tremendously.

Peter Thomson was a stylish, economical golfer who exhibited an unflappable temperament. His superb ball control and acute golfing brain won him five Open Championships between 1954 and 1965. Whenever I observed Thomson at work, he always left me with the lasting impression that golf is an easy game if it is played intelligently.

For as long as I can remember, Gary Player has been an inspiring, gutsy player, as well as being an articulate proselytizer of his strongly held beliefs. On the cusp of seventy, Gary remains a formidable competitor. However, even though I might continue to be in awe of every word that Gary Player utters, I would prefer to play my golf in the Peter Thomson style.

Having become used to travelling faster than the speed of light, I still managed to feel some impatience for our journey to Australia to be over. To whet our appetites and tantalize us even further, Bob Jones had an unanticipated change of plan in mid-flight, deciding to make a brief stopover in New Zealand, a golf destination that I knew precious little about.

Limerick men normally revere New Zealand for its rugby players, but Tail Gunner and I were more impressed by its champion golfers. Bob Charles is one of the all-time great short-game exponents and a former Open champion (1963), who, as he approaches seventy years of age, can still break par consistently. Simon Owen came within a whisker of winning the 1978 Open Championship at St Andrews and is now a stalwart of the European Seniors Tour. It was only at the 69th hole that Owen was finally cornered and devoured by a marauding Golden Bear. Before becoming solid performers and winners on the USPGA Tour, Phil Tataurangi and Michael Campbell (US Open winner 2005) helped their country to win the prestigious Eisenhower Trophy (World Team Amateur Championship) at Marine Drive Golf Club, Vancouver, in 1992. Frank Nobilo and Greg Turner are both stylish, intelligent golfers whom I have long admired. The Kiwi system for developing young golfing talent is highly respected around the world.

The Jones Express touched down at Paraparaumu Beach on the Kapiti Coast on the North Island, 35 miles north of Wellington. Similar to Royal Lytham and St Anne's in Lancashire, the Paraparaumu course does not actually overlook the ocean, but is nevertheless every inch the classic links layout, featuring small greens and undulating, fast, firm fairways. The course was designed by Alister Mackenzie's former Australian associate Alex Russell and is much appreciated by the locals, who only in recent years have been obliged to share its pleasures with a steadily growing number of visitors from overseas.

Cambridge-educated Russell won the Australian Amateur Championship in 1924. Upon graduation he became a career diplomat and high-ranking civil servant. As private secretary to several Australian prime ministers, Russell often travelled to England on state business, but he never left home without his golf clubs, frequently finding the time to compete in the British Amateur Championship or whatever other tournaments could be fitted into his busy schedule. Sporadically, Russell competed in the annual President's Putter competition at Rye, where he met Mackenzie, also a Cambridge man. Influenced by their common background, the two became friends.

When the committee of the Royal Melbourne Golf Club invited Mackenzie to work on their course in 1928, Mac invited Alex Russell to be part of his team; indeed, he went so far as to offer Russell an associate partnership in his firm. As already mentioned, Mac did not like to linger. When Jack Fleming was busy elsewhere, Mac enlisted somebody locally whom he could trust to keep an eye on things after he had left a site. Another attraction from Mac's point of view was that Russell was independently wealthy and was not overly demanding in regard to fees. Often strapped for cash himself, Mac may also have hoped that Russell might become an investor in his enterprises. As things turned out, the members of Royal Melbourne GC were so impressed with Russell that he was put in sole charge of the design work on their new East Course in 1930. Mac was thousands of miles away in California; bringing him back to Australia was considered too expensive an undertaking, especially when they could recruit such a good substitute on their very own doorstep.

Paraparaumu is packed tightly into a small area and every inch of it is used. At 6,600 yards it is eminently playable by all grades of golfers and, apart from Mac, we proved it by playing the most difficult hole (13th) in par figures. At just under 450 yards, and without a bunker in sight, it requires solid, straight hitting. That is easier to say than to accomplish, because success is largely dependent on finding an elusive flat lie on a roller-coaster fairway. The green is cunningly placed on a sand hill with deep run-offs in all directions, while behind the green the magnificent backdrop of mountains (snow-capped in winter), with their ever-changing colours, makes it difficult to keep one's head down. Deep fairway swales foreshorten the distance to be covered and also render running the ball on to the putting surface virtually impossible.

Playing into a stiff wind, club selection did not require much deliberation on anybody's part; everyone automatically played 'furniture', as Jones quaintly called his persimmon brassie. My fairway club, on the other hand, was made of twenty-first-century steel.

The 17th at Paraparaumu is a classic conundrum. A split fairway beckoned us to play down the direct route to shorten the second shot, but we soon realized that this angle of attack made the approach into the skewed green a more elusive target than if we had taken the longer route.

'In golf, one is always learning,' sighed Jones, who made the error of being too aggressive with his tee-shot; that led him into diagonally overshooting the green and for once failing to match par.

Outside the simple but welcoming Paraparaumu clubhouse we met the club professional, Alan Currie, who told us bluntly that we could not think of leaving New Zealand without at least looking at the Cape Kidnapper's course at Hawke's Bay. Because of the magnificent views along the coastline, we all decided to eschew our normal time-tunnel means of travel and go by road in a people-carrier jeep instead. On reaching Hawke's Bay, I thought for a brief second or two that we were back at the Old Head Links at Kinsale. The similarities were uncanny, except that at Cape Kidnapper's one has to play over the tops of exotic tea trees that are not part of the scene in County Cork. I could not resist hitting a ball into the sea, 500 feet below, to measure the hang-time. Golfing at Cape Kidnapper's is as exhilarating as playing on the very edge of the Earth.

After this all too brief visit to New Zealand, we left for the windswept, south-eastern coast of Australia. There we found a Mackenzie golf course that was as dramatic and exciting as anything yet seen on our whirlwind tour. We alighted on the 5th fairway at New South Wales Golf Club, overlooking Botany Bay where Captain James Cook sailed the *Endeavour* around the rocks on his way to discovering Australia in 1770.

Mac was quick to point out that the golf course relies very much, if not entirely, on the force and direction of the wind to defend itself. Three crunched metals and a bit to cover the 515 yards one day could turn into a drive and a short iron flick another. If the conditions are right, a golf ball has been known to run over 100 yards down this fairway. Similar to the stunning backdrops at Cypress Point, the ocean does not come into play but the beauty of the surroundings are capable of distracting the grimmest grinder. Given the natural endowments of the terrain, almost anybody could have designed this wonderful golf hole, but it was Mac's good fortune to have done so and he was proud of it.

His pride was about to grow. The course architect unleashed his almighty best drive over the brow of an intimidating rise of ground. Out of our sight, Mac's ball became turbo-charged as it was catapulted forward by the downhill gradient, firm turf and following breeze. The ball ran 80 yards before stumbling to a halt within an easy mid-iron reach of the green. Whoever said 'thin can win' is correct. Mac's skulled second shot ran unerringly to within 15 feet of the cup. After sinking the eagle putt, Mac accepted our congratulations without a hint of embarrassment. Ignoring his outrageous luck, he was soon telling all and sundry that he was 'very satisfied indeed' with his work here. His good humour stretched to heaping fulsome praise on local architects Eric Apperly and Alex Russell, whom he acknowledged had made 'a few significant modifications' to his original design.

When we walked from the 5th green on to the 6th tee, a stunning par 3 hole that runs parallel to the rocky cliff edge, Mac announced that he was going to try to emulate US President Bill Clinton, who had back-to-back birdies on these two holes during a private visit with Greg Norman some years earlier. The former President has a well-chronicled taste for classic golf courses. Clinton was hugely enthusiastic about New South Wales Golf Club; he and Greg Norman played until darkness fell while First Lady Hillary waited impatiently in Air Force One for her husband to join her for their journey home.

Our next port of call was Royal Melbourne Golf Club. Augusta notwithstanding, RMGC might arguably be Alister Mackenzie's greatest achievement in golf architecture. It was a bright and sunny 75°F with a frisky 20mph wind when we teed off: fabulous golfing conditions. We were granted the rare privilege of being permitted to play the normally forbidden (except on special occasions) Composite Course that takes twelve holes from the West Course and six holes from the East. Many keen students of golf architecture are of the opinion that these specific eighteen holes are the best golf available anywhere.

'I am not in the slightest surprised to hear that,' sniffed the architect haughtily. 'Royal Melbourne was the perfect canvas for me to exhibit the full range of my golf philosophies. I revelled in the rolling ground that facilitated wide fairways and dramatic fairway bunkering. Play Royal Melbourne the correct way and it will reward you. On the other hand, it will punish the foolish and unskilful without mercy. Those good enough to challenge the visible hazards by playing close to them are rewarded on every occasion, because they will have found the optimum line to the green. The fairway bunkering on my courses may appear highly visible and straightforward, but anyone who overplays the safety factor and strays too far from the optimum line will find that their next shot becomes progressively more difficult. Usually, my fairway bunkers are put in with framing and aesthetic purposes in mind, but I like to make my green-side bunkering as severe as the topography will allow. The nearer you get to the cup, the more difficult the game should be.'

Fleming pulled me to one side and whispered in my ear, 'One of Mac's biggest selling points to any promoter was what he termed "finality". But it is a fact that many of Mackenzie's designs blossomed without him being present to oversee the final completion and, of course, we should not forget that all of his courses are subject to inevitable evolution.

'Take Augusta. Over the years, no golf course has been tweaked and altered as much. Even the routing was altered by Clifford Roberts when he flip-flopped the nines after the first Invitational (Masters) Tournament. Seventy years on, Augusta is still considered to be Mac's course, but the hands of many others have influenced its maturation. I can assure you from experience that Mac's drawings were impressionistic art aimed at impressing investors rather than giving fellows like me, who had to do the hard graft of shaping the ground, precise instructions. I want to tell you that Alex Russell and Mick Morcom, the RMGC head green keeper, were geniuses in their own right who never received enough credit for what was achieved here.'

We were having a delightful round of golf without seeing another soul on the course besides ourselves until we reached the 15th green, where we were astonished to run into a befuddled, hot-and-bothered-looking Ernie Els from South Africa, foostering behind the green, practising chipping.

'Say Ernie, what y'all doing so far from Cape Town?' enquired Bob Jones, as friendly as you like.

'I could ask something similar of you, Mr Jones! Actually, I'm trying to figure out how I managed to allow one of the greatest opportunities of my career to slip from my grasp. Starting this hole in the Heineken Classic in 2004 I needed only one more birdie and three pars to break the magic sixty barrier. After a perfect drive, I managed to make a complete mess of this straightforward hole. I am still not sure why it happened, but I certainly blew it!' said a baffled Ernie sadly shaking his head in disbelief.

'Imagine that! Somebody almost breaking sixty on your greatest course. What do you think of that, Mac?' challenged Jack Fleming, a touch belligerently.

'Well, if y'all don't mind, gentlemen, that is one blow-by-blow that I would not mind listening to; partly because it will not take too long!' said Jones with a smile.

'Come on, Ernie, in your own words please. Tell us how you did it – or, to be more accurate, didn't do it,' implored Fleming.

'Okay. I'll try to get through this as quickly and as painlessly as possible,' said the blushing South African.

'1st (354 yards): 2-iron, sand-iron 20 feet past the hole, two putts. Par 4.

'2nd (498 yards): Mediocre drive to the right; got lucky and found a good lie. Had a perfectly open shot to the flag from there; 7-iron to left edge of the green, two putts from 60 feet. Birdie 4.

'3rd (176 yards): Nuked an 8-iron to about 18 feet past the cup, holed that one. Birdie 2.

'4th (450 yards): fairway metal off the tee, a smooth 9-iron to 18 feet and two-putted. Par 4.

'5th (332 yards): blasted the driver just short of the green; pitched up to about 8 feet and made it. Birdie 3.

'6th (439 yards): 2-iron; 8-iron to 4 feet, made it. Birdie 3. I wish golf were always that easy!

'7th (382 yards): 3-iron, 8-iron to 5 feet, missed it. Par 4. It was too early in the round to think of fifty-nine – but looking back, geez!

'8th (201 yards): 6-iron to 3 feet; it was the best shot I hit all day and it was the source of my momentum. When I holed the putt for a birdie 2, I knew I was on my way to a really low score.

'9th (557 yards): big drive and 3-iron to about 7 feet behind the hole and made it. I had 233 to the front and the hole was cut 29 back. Eagle 3.

'10th (483 yards): driver, 7-iron through the back edge, two-putted from 30 feet. Birdie 4.

'11th (147 yards): 8-iron to 14 feet left of the hole. Made it for another birdie 2.

'12th (304 yards): 3-iron off the tee left me with 65 yards in. Pitched up to about 3 feet and made it. Birdie 3. At this point fifty-nine crossed my mind for the first time.

'13th (454 yards): 3-metal, 5-iron to 5 feet; made it. Another birdie 3.

'14th (464 yards): 3-metal (again); 5-iron (again) to 15 feet and made that (again). Birdie 3. That's twelve-under after fourteen holes. Now I knew that breaking sixty was definitely on. Stupidly, I began thinking ahead, wondering where the next birdie might come from.

'15th (438 yards): an unnecessarily aggressive 2-iron ran out of fairway on the right (first mistake); out of a hot lie my 9-iron approach bounced through the green on the left into a gnarly lie (second mistake). Out of the poor lie, I wasn't able to achieve much control and only managed to scramble the chip to 8 feet above the hole (third mistake). Out of position, I did not go near holing the putt (fourth mistake). Antelope dust! A bogey 5. Still don't know why it happened but it hurts to think about it!'

'Of course it is easy for me to say after the event, but it is perfectly obvious how it happened,' said Jones, who had listened intently to every nuance of Ernie's blow-by-blow description. 'You were trying too hard and your muscles tensed up. You lost a bit of feel, that's all. Besides, this is the classic sucker punch hole. Everyone who has played this hole more than a few times knows that the second shot plays longer than it looks, but the green is pitched in such a way that any iron shot into it that carries past halfway up the green will bounce forward and run off the back. This is one of those birdie holes that you can never force.'

'I suppose you're right, Mr Jones,' said the disconsolate South African.

'16th (432 yards): 2-iron, wedge to about 18 feet, made that one for a birdie 3 and balanced the books.

'17th (428 yards): 2-iron, 9-iron short right. It wasn't a good shot. The tension was really getting to me. I was tightening up badly as you so wisely noticed. I did well to get out of there with a two-putt from 40 feet. Par 4.

'18th (442 yards): last chance. Driver, again tried too hard on my wedge approach. It went to the back edge of green about 25 feet away, two putts. Par 4.'

'Without any doubt that was a magnificent effort, Ernie, but from my point of view you must appreciate that I did not design my courses with players like you in mind. Back in the 1920s, 330-yard drives, 262-yard 3-irons and 210-yard 6-irons were not imaginable. A drive and a wedge to no. 18 at Royal Melbourne is obscene. Whatever equipment you were using should never have been allowed,' declared a grudging but admiring Mac.

'Nor should we forget that in our day the wedge did not even exist,' Jack Fleming pitched in.

'All right, let's pack it up boys!' interjected Jones. 'That's all we have time for down under. I'll give Tail Gunner the final choice of destination before we go back to Doughmore Beach for a swim. Where will it be?'

'Before going back to Doonbeg, could we ask the Golf Nut to show us the best of some of the recent developments in Irish golf, please?' asked Tail Gunner.

9

Tail Gunner's Tour

FOR THIRTY YEARS and more, the late Joe Carr dominated the amateur golf scene in Ireland. In 1961, Joe came within a whisker of reaching the final round of match play in the US Amateur at Pebble Beach, but a blond, crew-cut, bulldog-like youngster from Ohio State University, by the name of Jack William Nicklaus, rode roughshod over everybody and won the title for the second time before embarking on his as yet unequalled rampage of professional majors.

Because the rewards in pro golf are so enormous these days, a dominant, lifelong amateur career is no longer as attractive as it once was. In fact, nowadays the more successful the amateur is the more likely his career will be cut short. Records are made to be broken, but there is no chance that Carr's forty Irish national and provincial championships will ever be eclipsed. Nobody that successful could afford to decline the riches on offer in professional golf these days. Carr's career reached its pinnacle in 1960 when he won the British Amateur for the third time – an achievement that he had targeted well in advance by the undertaking of a previously unheard of training regime.

Furthermore, Carr was a contender in the 1960 centenary Open Championship at St Andrews won by Kel Nagle. Back then all competitors played two pre-championship qualifying rounds before the tournament proper got under way. At the end of the week Joe had the best total for the six rounds played, but unfortunately for him his two preliminary scores did not count.

Joe Carr played golf with an arrogant swagger and infectious good humour that intimidated all but the strongest of opponents. By no means the straightest of hitters, Joe could demoralize the opposition by managing to recover from 'impossible' situations. With hands as big as shovels and Houdini-like powers of escape, Joe could emerge unscathed from the nether regions of any golf course time after time.

Late in life, Joe Carr found another way to leave his mark on the game. He helped to design two excellent golf courses: the unique Old Head Links at Kinsale in County Cork, and Dromoland Castle in County Clare, only 15 miles from Tail Gunner's home in Limerick city.

For almost a thousand years the 28,000 acres of prime agricultural land at Dromoland was the ancestral home of true blue royal princes of Ireland: the O'Brien clan. That was until 1543, when King Henry VIII forced Murrough O'Brien, a direct descendant of Brian Boru, the eleventh-century warrior king of a peaceful and united Ireland, to surrender his royal heritage. In the early nineteenth century, Edward O'Brien built the residential-style castle that exists today.

During its long history, one of Dromoland's most colourful inhabitants was the legendary Red Mary O'Brien (1615–86). Renowned for her beautiful red hair, Mary was married three times. In a life of considerable excitement and conflict, Red Mary's greed for property seems to have grown with each of her marriages. At the age of fifteen, she was wed to Daniel Neylon, a gentleman thrice her age who owned considerable property in north Clare. Widowed in her twenties and with four young children, she took Conor O'Brien as husband number two. This marriage was happy and productive. In their twelve years together eight more children and vast tracts of land were acquired. However, in his continual struggles with invading English settlers and Irish neighbours, Conor O'Brien found himself in the wrong place at the wrong time and was slain. To help protect her property, Red Mary married for a third time. As the estate continued to grow, the union with an ambitious English military officer, John Cooper, who had served under Cromwell, brought a thirteenth child. When Charles II ascended to the throne in England, the Cooper–O'Brien alliance found itself once more on the wrong side of an argument. Threatened with confiscation and possible execution, Cooper made off with as much as he could muster of a considerable fortune. Red Mary stood her ground and somehow managed, against the odds, to retain her home and most of her property. She is buried beside her favourite husband, Conor, in nearby Ennis Abbey.

A golf course has been part of the Dromoland demesne since 1961. Long before the Carr redesign, Tail Gunner and I had played there. We often expressed the view that the rolling land, magnificent lake, streams and thousands of mature trees had unlimited potential. Although the new layout is instantly recognizable, many of the original holes have been transformed. Perhaps the most remarkable work took place at the 4th (490 yards) and 5th (405 yards), two holes that were previously dull, featureless slogs. By digging out a deep channel along the left-hand side and allowing it to grow wild with fescue, then raising and reshaping the two fairways and greens with the removed dirt, two nondescript golf holes have become highly attractive ones. The rearranged final three holes are savagely difficult. There is a completely new 16th hole (455 yards, par 4) channelled out of rock and forest. The 17th hole (220 yards, par 3) requires a carry of 190 yards across a ball-devouring swamp. The 18th hole (580 yards, par 5) has been altered to a mirror image of its former self and now goes around the rim of the lake from left to right. A large Sequoia tree dominates the narrowest part of a funnelled fairway, squeezing the lay-up area before one is allowed the space for a clear crack at the green abutting the lake.

'That final walk on to the 18th green under the shadow of the castle with the lake lapping close by is hard to beat. Where to next?' asked the delighted Tail Gunner, after he had curled a teasing 15-footer across the slope into the cup for a superbly played birdie.

'Ireland already has the largest number of seaside links courses in the world. Why don't we pay a visit to an "inland links" designed by the Scot Colin Montgomerie?' I suggested.

On entering the grounds of Carton House, near bustling Maynooth Town in County Kildare, one cannot escape the overwhelming feeling of history. The beautiful manor house, its gardens and 1,100 acres of superbly preserved countryside, situated a mere 20 miles from the hurly-burly of metropolitan Dublin, was from 1176 until 1920 the ancestral home of successive Lord FitzGeralds, who, as Earls of Kildare and Dukes of Leinster, ruled Ireland for generations.

In 1747, James, the 20th Earl, married Lady Emily Lennox, daughter of the Duke of Richmond. To this day, Emily is responsible for much of the landscaping and gardens. She created the Chinese room where Queen Victoria slept during a famous visit in 1849. Emily also supervised the unique decoration of the shell cottage that overlooks the 14th green on the O'Meara Course. One of Emily's twenty-three children was the Irish patriot Lord Edward FitzGerald, leader of the 1798 Irish rebellion. Edward himself is responsible for the Italian–Swiss decoration of the main reception area of the manor house. Carton House remained in the control of the FitzGeralds until the 1920s, when the 7th Duke disastrously sold his birthright to a moneylender in order to settle some gambling debts. Third in line of succession, he believed that he would never inherit, but one brother was killed in the First World War, while another suffered a premature death from a brain tumour. What the FitzGeralds might think of the current situation on their lands is mind-boggling – though Lord Edward, the most famous of them, was a keen sportsman, particularly adept in horsemanship and archery; it is conceivable that he might well have taken to golf in different circumstances.

There are two golf courses at Carton House, each entirely different to the other. The O'Meara Course is heavily sand-trapped and tree-lined, with a number of energy-sapping climbs. The main feature is the river Rye, which snakes through a beautiful valley in the back nine, creating features on holes 14 to 16 that would not be out of place at Augusta National.

Apart from the first tee-shot, trees hardly come into play on the Montgomerie Course. A prairie-like feeling of wide-open space, rolling land, large fast greens and severe sand traps must have been inspired by St Andrews.

As we made our way along the entrance drive, straining to take in everything we could see, we noticed the course architect hitting balls on the large practice ground – an event in itself, as Colin is not famous for whacking balls.

We did not hesitate to approach Monty and, getting straight down to business, Tail Gunner asked, 'An inland links sounds like an oxymoron. What gave you that idea?'

'That's a bit of a cheek, but never mind!' replied a surprisingly affable Monty. 'I suppose you can get away with such things in Ireland!'

I nearly said I wish you smiled like that more often on the golf course, but I thought the better of it. The guy was trying to be friendly, so why risk spoiling it?

'Ireland has so many outstanding seaside links that I thought it was time it had one inland too,' said Monty, his jovial mood seeming to continue. 'This course is as close to seaside golf as you will find 30 miles away from the sea. Whenever I come here, I always half-expect to see waves churning beyond the walls that surround the property.

'Because the course is virtually treeless, it appears wide open. The idea of having room to curve the flight of the ball appeals to me, but be warned: you have to be careful to plot a safe path through those fairway undulations, large bunkers, plunging swales and run-offs. Designing bunkers that would punish even the most skilled was one of my priorities. I wanted bunkers that are genuine hazards and would cost a player at least half a shot if he went into any of them,' Monty declared with a threatening glint in his eye.

'In every instance, my greens here have to be approached from specific parts of the fairway to obtain maximum results. My favourite holes are the downhill par 3, the 17th, where accurate club selection and some bravery are called for; while the shortish par 4 13th shows that a hole less than 350 yards can be brutally difficult. Playing on to that elusive surface, even with a wedge, is a stern challenge.'

When we had concluded our round, we were all in agreement that Monty's assessment of his own work was reasonable and fair, except that Tail Gunner and I agreed between us that our favourite holes were the 10th and 15th.

Following one of the most expensive construction projects ever undertaken to develop a golf course in Europe, the Smurfit Course at the K Club is now maturing beautifully. Only two years after it was opened for play, and one year after being first introduced to the golfing public by the hosting of the 2004 Smurfit European Open, the course has settled down to be a superbly maintained challenge.

Featuring elemental ruggedness alongside spectacular water features, the course is named after Dr Michael Smurfit, who was one of the key players in bringing the 2006 Ryder Cup to Ireland. It loses absolutely nothing in comparison with the more famous Palmer Course, on the other side of the river Liffey. The two courses could hardly be more different to each other in appearance and personality.

As we approached the 16th green, we stopped for a moment to chat with resort superintendent Gerry Byrne. It was immediately obvious that this man loves his job, which he decribes with enthusiasm. 'Tending a golf course is a neverending, evolving process. For me it is a passion, embracing joy and satisfaction every day. Because a golf course is a living thing, it requires constant attention: one can never rest. Matters can get out of control very quickly. Looking after everything properly is a new challenge every day.

'From the beginning we deliberately set out to present two entirely different golfing challenges here. The Palmer Course is heavily tree-lined in a formal, orderly way and looks extremely tight and difficult, but there is more room than you might think.

The Smurfit Course is quite the opposite, appearing wide open in a rugged, linksy style, with its enormous undulations, wild grasses and gorse, but the optimum lines of play are painstakingly worked out; any deviation from the correct path will exert a price.

'When we began excavating the site, we moved a staggering 1.3 million cubic feet of earth – a huge feat in engineering. One side-benefit of moving all that earth is that we now have a Stadium Course, which, ironically, may have been ideally suited to hosting the Ryder Cup matches. The project we undertook at the 7th was so vast that we recycled the supply of water at a rate of 15,000 gallons per minute: a massive exercise. There are 14 acres of lakes on the final six holes alone.'

In this age of saturation TV coverage, it is hard to believe that John A. Mulcahy's efforts to put Waterville on the golfing map by organizing the Kerrygold Classic took place at a time when there was no BBC, let alone Sky, coverage in Ireland. Back in the 1970s, Tail Gunner and I were annual visitors to the Waterville Golf Links for the August Open Week. The magnificence of the golf links, the superb food in the restaurants and the friendly atmosphere around the town made for a great short-break holiday.

In 1975, to sate our appetites for studying famous, exotic golfers, Tail Gunner and I made the long trip to Ballinskelligs Bay in order to observe the legendary technique of 'Slamming Sammy' Snead at close quarters. But it was the primitiveness of the coverage of Ireland's national TV station (Telifis Eireann) that I remember best. A little cameo that we observed at first hand illustrates the point. The late Brendan O'Reilly, a gallant, American-trained anchorman in the TE sports department, arrived at Waterville with a single cameraman in tow. Brendan was no golf expert, but he did have a clear objective and that was to interview Snead. The weather was so dreadful that O'Reilly's cameraman, for his own health and safety as much as for the sake of his expensive equipment, refused point blank to leave the sanctuary of the clubhouse. Peering through the downpour from the relative safety of the bar, the lens was barely able to capture a few ghost-like figures moving erratically about in the lashing rain. After completing his round, a thoroughly saturated, dripping-wet Sam Snead was ushered into the crowded hallway of the clubhouse to be greeted by the impeccable O'Reilly. What the Irish TV audience saw next on their screens would not have been out of place in a horror movie: a head and shoulders view of a thoroughly disgruntled Sam Snead wearing a bright red, floppy-brimmed bucket hat. The hat was never intended for such hardship. Red dye streamed down Sam's face and it looked like blood.

'How did you play today, Sam?' O'Reilly asked cheerily.

'Crap!'

'How do you enjoy playing in Ireland?' O'Reilly positively beamed.

'Does it ever stop raining in this goddam country?'

Clearly a man not to be thrown off by the (edited) expletives that littered Sam's colourful speech, O'Reilly ventured on. 'Sam, you were playing with Dr Michael Dargan, president of Aer Lingus, today. How did Dr Dargan play?'

'Lousy. He couldn't hit an elephant in the butt with a tennis racket!'

Cut. O'Reilly knew he was beaten by a combination of the appalling weather and Snead's vile humour.

I saw the episode differently. First, I was delighted to discover that Sam Snead was flesh and blood and prone to a bad mood coming off a golf course. Second, Sam was as bald as a coot and no taller than myself. Third, he could certainly out-swear me; and fourth, I had the confounded cheek to believe that in spite of our respective pedigrees I might have given Sam a run for his money in the appalling conditions.

Then out of the blue the rain-lashed audience witnessed a stunning exhibition of athleticism from Snead. For a good-humoured bet struck with Jack Mulcahy, without breaking stride or falling flat on his back and breaking his neck, Sam spring-kicked the overhead frame of the doorway to the locker room while still shod in his steel-studded golf shoes.

In 1968, Irishman John A. Mulcahy, who had a personal fortune in pharmaceuticals in the USA, purchased 300 acres of dunes overlooking Ballinskelligs Bay at the edge of Waterville village. The choice of site was inspired. Mulcahy quickly formed a triumvirate of unique brainpower with Ireland's most prolific architect, Eddie Hackett, and Claude Harmon. Harmon was a former Augusta Masters Champion and the head professional at Winged Foot in New York. These days he is even more famous as the father of Butch Harmon. Hackett was added to the ticket to provide expertise in Irish conditions and to undertake the hard daily graft of supervising the construction work.

Shortly before Jack Mulcahy passed away in 1987, Wall Street executive Jay Connolly, on behalf of a small group of Irish-Americans who loved both Ireland and Waterville, negotiated the purchase of the Mulcahy family home (Waterville House) and the golf course. Fully appreciating Jack's wishes, the new owners guaranteed that they would carry on the same vision.

Jack Mulcahy used to say that the secret to his success in business was 'to gather the best people around me; tell them the objectives; loosen the reins and let them rip!' That is precisely what the Waterville Board did. They sought out whom they considered to be the best architect to advise them. When they got their man, they presented him with a short wish list. It is a compliment to Tom Fazio that it is virtually impossible to discern any changes from holes nos. 3 to 5 and nos. 8 to 14 – a total of ten holes, but no. 11 is actually the only hole that has been left untouched and there is every chance that that omission may not last too far into the future either.

'I can see that the front nine has been given an entirely new personality. Waterville is now the total golf experience, with each nine, front and back, complimenting the other beautifully. Special attention seems to have been given to creating an almost perfect balance of left to right and right to left play. There is not a single weak hole,' said Tail Gunner admiringly.

'And just think that all the Waterville Board asked for was a new practice range, a better 6th and 7th, and some advice on improving bunker consistency,' I said.

'Take the first hole,' I went on. 'Without changing the location of the tee or green, the hole is now highly intimidating. The ubiquitous stream on the right remained untouched, but by enhancing its visibility it gives the impression of being closer to the line of play. That illusion forces itself into the golfer's consciousness, causing a nervous first shot of the day on a hole that is laughingly named, "The Last Easy!"

'Most of Fazio's work took place on the front nine, but the last three holes are quite spectacular: scenic and brutal. The 16th hole (386 yards, par 4) has been designed to take better advantage of its unique site with its surrounding views of land, sea and mountains. The fairway has been raised and is now fully visible from the tee; a deep low in the fairway just beyond the landing area and a severely contoured green has added strategy and precision to a deceptively difficult golf hole that allows the golfer a full view of beach and town.

'The 17th (Mulcahy's Peak), par 3, is the founder's pride and joy. Jack Mulcahy used this high tee as a "lookout tower" to gaze over the course, but it is no place for faint hearts, with a testing long-iron tee-shot over inhospitable country to a raised green close to the cliff edge awaiting.'

As I finished speaking, Jones played another masterful 2-iron to within easy two-putt distance, making little of my graphic descriptions. Finally, to stand on the 18th tee at Waterville is a nerve-jangling experience, with 594 yards (par 5) of endless trouble to be avoided before you reach the sanctuary of the clubhouse. A brave golfer must trust his swing from tee to green here.

The late Eddie Hackett is regarded as the patron saint of Irish golf. Tales of his devotion to the game's development are legendary. If ever a man put personal satisfaction ahead of financial gain, it was Hackett. For much of his life he put his heart and soul into building golf courses for meagre financial reward, but what a legacy he left behind!

Long before the sainted Eddie ever came to Enniscrone in County Sligo, another Irish saint, Patrick, walked across the future fairways on his way to visit the holy island of Bartra. Legend also says that in AD 789 a company of Vikings landed on Enniscrone Beach, only to be met by savage resistance from the local O'Dowda clan. The hapless Vikings were slaughtered, their bodies piled high and buried under a huge mound of sand named Cnoc Na gCorp (Hill of Bodies). This stupendous sand dune, the largest on any golf course in Ireland, looms eerily over the 14th fairway.

Hackett believed in working with the natural flow of the land; not for him the attitude of forcing land to bend to his will. He achieved this by rarely designing a straight hole and by building quirky greens. Sometimes Hackett's work is dismissed as primitive, but it has to be said in his defence that he was rarely allowed off a tight financial leash to do as he might really have wished.

When Hackett set about upgrading Enniscrone in 1974, he must have pined to be allowed to go more deeply into the dunes; that missed opportunity must have been heartbreaking. Thirty years later, the arrival of the Celtic Tiger provided the resources to make such an ambitious scheme possible, but it was an Englishman, Donald Steel, who was chosen to do the honours.

When our group reached the 12th tee, at the furthest extremities of the course, I pointed towards a narrow island only a short distance away that sits in the centre of the Moy river estuary where it spills into the North Atlantic Ocean, and said, 'That is the so-called holy island of Bartra visited by St Patrick back in the fifth century. It belongs to Nick Faldo now. Nick has promised to handcraft a golf course over there to match anything yet seen. It is likely that he is over there right now, fishing rod in hand.'

Jealousy is part of the territory of being a champion. Making the opposition feel uncomfortable through psychological intimidation was part of what Faldo did best in tournament golf. These tactics did not endear him to everybody, but they brought him much success. It must have been highly frustrating for Faldo that technology rather than any loss of ability or desire brought his days of winning major tournaments to a halt. These days, Nick spends most of his time designing golf courses and commentating on TV with a wicked sense of humour that has taken audiences by surprise.

When he described Bartra as the most magical property he had ever seen, it was unclear whether it was his keen fisherman instincts or his golfing ambitions that were uppermost. We were soon to find out, because Bob Jones once again demonstrated his magical powers of transportation and we found ourselves walking up behind an intense, bent-over figure peering into the rush of water, unaware of our arrival.

Without the formality of an introduction, Mac opened the conversation by demanding, 'What exactly do you mean by handcrafting a golf course?'

'The golf links I envisage here would be a return to how golf courses were created in the golden age of golf design; it would not be so much a case of building a course as discovering it. My goal is to draw as much as I can from the island's natural beauty. It means working with, and being sensitive to, the site's existing topography and utilizing the natural features. It means building a golf course in the old-fashioned way, moving very little earth and not being dependent on modern machinery. It also means doing much of the work by feel and instinct out in the field as opposed to in the office with a CAD computer. A handcrafted golf course is one that looks as if it "belongs" – as if it has been part of the landscape for centuries.'

'When building a golf course, Nick, do you have a recognizable style?' Tail Gunner asked.

'The golf courses I design are essentially strategic in nature. I always try to combine creativity with originality, but I don't regard myself as having a definitive "style" as such. I would hate to think that there is such a thing as a "typical Nick Faldo course". I believe the site should dictate the general concept rather than imposing preconceived ideas. Golf courses should look as natural as possible, and, whilst they should challenge and inspire, they should always be playable and fair. When a golfer finishes his round, the ones that really stick in his mind are always going to be the ones he found beautiful to look at and enjoyable to play.'

Bob Jones asked, 'Does one have to be a highly skilled practitioner to be a successful designer?'

'Not necessarily. Many of the finest architects were only moderate players. The perfect golf course is surely one that inspires, challenges and is engaging for every level of player. But I do believe that my experience and appreciation of strategy and shot-making gives me an advantage.'

Mac was back in again with a question that seemed to intrigue Faldo, because he became much more animated.

'Do you regard golf-course architecture as an artistic endeavour or is it merely landscaping on a larger scale?'

'There is definitely art in creating a golf course, because much of the pleasure to be derived from a game of golf comes from the surroundings and setting. One of the reasons I enjoy design so much is the challenge of balancing what the finished product will look like, its aesthetic appeal, with how it will play and its shot-making values. I certainly think there's an art to that. Furthermore, a good golf course will withstand the test of time no matter what changes in equipment come along. Some extra length may be needed in places, but that is all. Length is not the only criteria for deciding the greatness or otherwise of a golf course. Art has definitely influenced the way I look at a golf course.'

'That's an admirable concept. I hope you succeed, Nick,' said Mackenzie, who had obviously found a kindred spirit.

Before another word could be spoken, Tail Gunner interjected and requested, 'Now Bob, please take us to County Wicklow where the Pope Ruddy has handcrafted a diabolical golf links in his own image!'

10

Coming Home

NORMALLY YOU HEAR Pat 'The Pope' Ruddy before you see him. He is a large-framed man with a big voice and a ready smile, who, as a working journalist from a fairly modest background, conceived the outrageous idea of owning his own personal golf fiefdom early in life. Anybody who knew of this ambition did not hold much hope of his ever having the resources to fulfil the dream; but even with the responsibility of rearing and educating a growing family, Pat was prepared to take unfathomable risks and make huge sacrifices.

Because of his eminent position in Irish golfing affairs and the autocratic but benevolent way he runs his golf empire, Ruddy is affectionately known throughout Ireland as 'The Pope'. If one were allowed only three words to describe him they would be: visionary, persistent and amiable. Having been told by the experts that land suitable for 'pure links golf' in Ireland was oversubscribed and had reached saturation point, Ruddy simply ignored them and went about his own business in his own way. On one of those long, bright summer days that we enjoy in the Emerald Isle more often than we are inclined to admit, Ruddy hired a helicopter and spent twelve unforgettable hours flying around the coast in search of his ideal piece of golfing property. He found what he was looking for 35 miles south of Dublin, at Brittas Bay in County Wicklow.

Although by no means a wealthy man, Ruddy managed to persuade a sceptical bank manager to help him purchase 220 acres with almost a mile of shoreline adjoining the Irish Sea. Taking an inordinate length of time to study the land before ever putting a shovel near it, Ruddy, piecemeal and single-handedly, set about the handcrafting of what he rather boldly named The European Club. The use of heavy earth-moving equipment was spurned as much for the expense involved as for the desire to craft something with his bare hands. Ruddy progressed his project so slowly and with so much attention to detail that the course that eventually emerged could truly be said to have evolved rather than been knocked into shape, in Jack Nicklaus's folksy parlance. As a result, all features are now beautifully proportioned and in perfect, natural harmony. The holes that are adjacent to the Irish Sea are basic and uncomplicated, but highly memorable.

There were advantages that Ruddy did not have the resources to do the job in a commercial manner. Satisfaction – earning an honest living and leaving a legacy, rather than making pots of money – has always been the objective anyway. Every time one goes to The European Club something new has happened. A new tee or bunker has appeared, or a fairway line has been altered. As time goes by, the changes become subtler. If in the current era of soaring green-fee tariffs some money is being earned, it is welcome but incidental. Ruddy credits another Irish golf promoter, Dr Michael Smurfit of the K Club, as the conduit that brought realistic, overdue money into Irish golf. To be fair to the often-criticized Dr Smurfit, he will reap his well-deserved reward only after the staging of the 2006 Ryder Cup matches at his K Club.

Everything about the game besots Pat Ruddy. He eats, sleeps and breathes golfing excellence. Having given back to the game more than he ever took out, the ambitions he has for his course remain steadfastly altruistic. Hailing from a cautious spending zone, the west of Ireland, Ruddy never lost sight of providing or receiving value for money. He understands expensive is not for everyone. But when one talks golf and golf tourism, one is talking luxury – degrees of luxury perhaps, but luxury none the less. Happily, Ireland has over 450 golf courses where one can get a game for a wide range of green fees. It is as good an *à la carte* menu as any, standing favourably beside any country in the world in terms of price range and quality.

'When compared with what is charged at top USA or UK venues, Ireland's like-with-like comparisons beat them like a drum,' Ruddy once boomed at me.

The European Club is run to Ruddy's own unique set of standards. The golf course takes no prisoners and has no mercy on the inept. On the scorecard, Ruddy's stated philosophy of making no apology to the thoughtless golfer, who might suffer hardship, is typical but in complete contrast to the fulsome welcome and friendly disposition that is bestowed upon visitors when they are not on the course. Ruddy delights in the fact that his golf course asks searching questions and sows confusion in the minds of fragile golfers.

Ruddy would never be inhibited by anyone in his own kingdom. He is never lost for a word; nor was he when, only to his mildest surprise, he espied me leading our small group of time-travellers through the entrance gate without extending the courtesy of advance notice.

'The keenness of golfers to play their game never surprises me, even if they have come from another world. Of course I'll fit you in. It's an honour and a privilege to have you all here. But first, come into the clubhouse and have breakfast while I clear the decks and make sure that the course is free ahead of you. There is not much point in owning the place if one cannot do this for special friends!' Ruddy declared with a broad smile.

While the rest of us enjoyed a substantial home-cooked breakfast of pork sausages, bacon, fried eggs, mushrooms, baked beans, piping hot tea and toast, O. B. Keeler, who until that moment had kept a discreet distance, went into full journalistic mode. He began by asking Ruddy how he had developed such an enormous love and respect for the game.

'My father was a keen player at a small course in the west of Ireland. My mother was a recreational player. It was what we did as a family and I loved it from the start. I quickly became engrossed reading Henry Longhurst's essay in the *Sunday Times* every week. I was further stimulated when the local library began to stock golf books, like Bob Jones's *Down the Fairway*, Ben Hogan's *Power Golf*, Tommy Armour's *How To Play Your Best Golf All the Time* and Sir Henry Cotton's *My Golfing Album*. As a family we devoured them all. Whenever my father and his friends failed to fill their Wednesday fourball, they would call me out of school to make up the numbers. What a great idea that was! Of course, other influences came into play very quickly, most of all that Cotton book, which introduced me to the glamour of international golf. Little did I know that I would end up as a personal friend of Sir Henry's, becoming his pupil and partner in course design. Then along came the TV shows, *All-Star Golf* and *Shell's Wonderful World of Golf*. They fired up my imagination to a huge degree. The dream of playing the game well and owning one's own golf course came sharply into focus around that time.'

Keeler dived in with another question: 'In the early 1960s, you had justifiable ambitions to be a player. When did you decide to alter your dreams and go in pursuit of new ones instead?'

'Not persisting as a serious but failing competitor was a smart move,' replied Ruddy. 'My mother persuaded me to go back to the books, saying that there was no money in golf. She was right, at the time, but was proved so wrong later. As a trainee reporter, I remember going up to Clontarf Golf Club on Sunday mornings and sitting under the tree at the first tee with Jack Quinn, the lovely old professional there, helping him to hand out cards and pencils to the members. Quinn and others I trusted, like Bob Wallace in Galway, expressed the view that there wasn't a living to be had out of golf, let alone golf journalism. In 1962 it was an understandable claim, because that year Peter Thomson was leading money-winner for the whole season with a haul of £5,764 sterling. Not exactly a king's ransom even in 1962. Allowing for inflation, it still compares in no way with the vast amounts of money earned these days. Back then, tournaments, including the

Open Championship, used to end on Fridays so that the pros could rush back to their shops in time to sell a few tees and balls to their members at the weekend. The centenary Open in 1960 was the first time that the championship ended on a Saturday and that was only because Friday's play was washed out.

'I adored reading about golf, so it was natural that I would be attracted to writing. I became possibly the first Irish person to devote himself one hundred per cent to writing professionally about golf and nothing else. It was a brave move, because the game was only just beginning to expand. I owe much to many editors around the world, but most of all to the late Aidan Pender, who gave me a huge break by inviting me to write five full broadsheet pages of golf every week in the *Evening Herald*.'

Mac's ears had pricked up at the mention of Henry Cotton and design. He was ready with the next question.

'How do you describe yourself then: golf writer, architect or promoter?

'I don't like being pigeonholed, nor do I believe in labels, but a combination of the first two, I reckon. I have always loved golf as a basic thing; by that I mean that I am not too keen on treating golf as a product or business attachment. For example, I take a jaundiced view of the over-hyped Ryder Cup, which is primarily in existence to make money for the Professional Golf Associations. It has been a big bonus to be able to work at many different aspects of the game as well as to play at it; that way one gets as close as possible to total immersion and one can understand all parts of it. I particularly love the design work on golf courses. It is the nearest you can get to creating something artistic if you have not a single artistic bone in your body. What better materials to work with than mother earth, with props such as oceans, mountains and sky? Have the opportunity to play a part in other people's lives, giving them nice places in which to enjoy little portions of their existences, hopefully for hundreds of years after one has shuffled on. I love writing too. It is always a release to talk through the keyboard. It doesn't talk back and one has the opportunity to work one's thoughts through to a conclusion without being interrupted or sidetracked.'

Keeler was obviously relishing this private conversation with a soul mate and said, 'You did what very few could do. You put your financial future at risk by dedicating your life to a crazy dream. Cliff Roberts and Bob Jones did something similar at Augusta National in the most difficult of economic circumstances imaginable after the Wall Street Crash. From your point of view has all the sacrifice been worth it?'

'Definitely a maybe! Who can look back on life and say they would play it exactly the same again? The path I chose brought the years forward very fast and landed me breathless and surprised on the doorstep of old age. Was it worth it? Well, I wanted it and I got it. As far as I know, the good Lord has given me only one life and my devotion to this place eliminated all other possibilities or pursuits from my life. Having you guys here today gives me hope that the best might yet be to come when I eventually cross over. Let's just say, I was fascinated by the battle and I love the satisfaction that I have gained from enduring. I'm happy.'

Jack Fleming seemed to be anxious to join in the conversation. 'Pat, you have built abroad as well as at home. Were there any discernible differences in the construction process overseas compared to what you experienced in Ireland?'

'What a question! Entire books have been devoted to this proposition, you know. It was exciting to be one of very few European architects to be employed to work in North America in modern times. Since the golden era of the early 1900s when the British brought the game across the pond, few have had that special trust given to them. To be asked to build thirty-six holes in the suburbs of a major city like Montreal was particularly rewarding; my task was to restore Montreal Island Golf Club, an old city course that once housed the Canadian Open, before it was ploughed up to make way for the Olympic stadium. I hope that it will come to be regarded as a fine course internationally, in due time. I learned a lot about local government and environmental issues in Canada.'

As quick as a flash, Mackenzie joined in to ask, 'How do you cope with cranky environmentalists who seem to mistrust and despise golf?'

'The questions get worse! That's a big issue – correctly so too. I admire greatly what many people are doing to protect the environment and I applaud them. But I also feel that some people are inclined to forget that this planet is for humans too. I cannot agree with those who insist that humans must live in clustered boxes with no privacy while thousands of acres are left free for the flora and fauna. It is sad to think that people were left to rot in the countryside when they had no electricity, no running water, no telephone, no radio, no television, no transportation. Now that they have all of these things, and a bit of money, country living is dying. People are being forced into towns, where they aren't even allowed to park a motorcar outside their own front doors. This policy cannot be right in Ireland, of all places, where our population is so small. We have an average of 135 people per square mile, whereas comparative figures show that Holland, Belgium and Germany have average population densities of 1,199, 805 and 611. If *they* are not poisoning each other and can survive, *we* should have no worries. The laws that may be needed in mainland Europe are not appropriate here. Of course everyone wants a clean environment, but some extremists give an honourable and correct range of sciences an aggressive and mean-minded image, which promotes antagonism and fear.'

Mackenzie knew that he had found a kindred spirit who spoke his own language, and he continued, 'What is your first aim when building a golf course?'

'Dry ground! I am a drainage maniac. There is no longer any excuse for soggy, waterlogged fields. We should be able to play golf in comfort all year through in this country. I am very proud of Castlecomer Golf Club in County Kilkenny: not the richest club in the world, but they took my advice and became one of the first in Ireland to install sand fairways, tees and greens. It will pay them well for generations to come. One worry is that too many revenue-hungry promoters follow the hotel and housing pattern, which crowds the golf in the worst way. Classic golf courses cannot be produced in this environment. You can never compromise in the pursuit of excellence. How can you out-art the best artists in course design if you have to adjust your plans to fit in a few extra houses?

'In Ireland, we are now in our own golden age of golf-course design. Our national stock of courses has doubled since 1980. It is phenomenal to think that within the past twenty years almost eighty of our nine-holers have been upgraded to eighteen. Almost all the work done is excellent, and Irishmen have done most of it. When I started out in the early 1970s, the only other Irish practitioner was Eddie Hackett. Now we have wonderful and consistent work being produced by Patrick Merrigan, Mel Flanagan, Ronan Branigan, Dr Arthur Spring, Ken Kearney and Christy O'Connor Junior to name but a few. I hope that Irish architects will always be persistent enough to demand the attention, respect and freedom that would automatically be accorded to so-called stars from overseas, begging present company's pardon – but I suppose you are out of the frame now, eh Mac?'

Breakfast eaten, it was time to go out and play. We were ushered to the 10th tee. Standing beside the back marker, I wondered how any of us would manage to reach the fairway, let alone the green, playing into the cold, stiff wind that was coming straight into our faces off the Irish Sea on this 490-yard par 4. Ruddy took up the conversation again.

'I don't know whether the guy was trying to flatter me or not, but when Tiger Woods stood right here on this spot a couple of years ago, he reacted exactly the same way as you are now. It happened on at least another half-dozen occasions throughout his round with his friend and mentor Mark O'Meara. Tiger looked at me, his eyes as big as saucers, and asked, 'Par 5, Pat?'

'Every time, I took great pleasure in disabusing him of that notion. "No Tiger, it's a par 4," I said with alacrity and some devilment. He feigned being flummoxed, but he managed to get every one of his fours all the same. He went around in sixty-seven – the best score ever recorded here. It's nice to have somebody with his pedigree hold your course record. What a fabulous talent and a really nice man to boot!' Ruddy obviously relished the memory.

Without anybody's daring suggest it or complain about it, we all moved forward 40 yards to the more reasonable white tee-marker and struck off. Each shot was greeted with booming praise or brutal jocularity. Ruddy declined to play along with us, claiming a hip injury. Instead, he appointed himself adviser, critic and cheerleader for each one of us in turn. Suffice to say we remained at the Brittas Bay venue longer than anywhere else on our short tour. Ruddy's golf course and his incessant golf talk were intoxicating.

We flinched at the precision demanded to find the 7th fairway and gasped when we stood on the elevated 12th tee and saw the mile-long stretch of golf holes ahead of us beside a dark and choppy Irish Sea. When we reached the magnificent 17th (432 yards, par 4), Jones put on a show and lashed a superb drive down into the plunging valley surrounded by heather, then followed it with a classic long iron into the stiff breeze on to the amphitheatre green. Ruddy was so delighted he positively roared above the wind.

'Two of the best shots I have ever seen, Tiger included! You may come here any time as my guest, Mr Jones. Anybody who can hit golf shots like that deserves the courtesy of my course for ever!'

After our whirlwind Irish tour, Tail Gunner and I arrived back at Doonbeg, where our adventure had started. Somehow, our companions did not manage to complete the relatively short hop across Ireland. Without any explanations or goodbyes, we found ourselves on our own once more.

In an ill-judged attempt to get a conversation going again, I turned to Tail Gunner and said, 'Did you hear that after fifteen years in the doldrums, out of the blue, I found an infallible model of the perfect swing, thanks to a visit to the USGA headquarters in Far Hills, New Jersey. There I encountered the Iron Byron Testing Machine. What a performer; such beautiful rhythm!

'Apparently, many years ago, the True Temper Company, which manufactures golf shafts, had the idea of building a mechanical golfer to test and research the company's products. A twenty-eight-year-old mechanical engineer named George Manning was put in charge of the project. The first thing he did was try to figure out what the perfect golf swing should look like. He took thousands of still photographs and miles of action film of top players. After months of research, it was decided that the best human model for the experiment would be Byron Nelson, a golfer who, although he had retired from competition in the early 1950s, was widely known as "the father of the modern golf swing".

'Watching the Iron Byron machine in action was mesmerizing. For about six weeks after I had seen it hit balls, I played at a level that I genuinely thought I would never achieve. My mind had been more or less closed to the idea that a better technique would, by itself, improve my performance. I had come to believe that my lifelong inability to fulfil my potential as a golfer was an aberration in temperament.'

Tail Gunner exploded. 'For heaven's sake, were you not listening to Jones on the 13th fairway a few hours ago? When will you realize that no game lends itself to so much analysis, so much loose talk and so much convoluted theorizing? Jones told you that tournament golf is a different game and getting ready for tournaments is primarily a mental challenge. He told you that what counts most in tournament golf is your emotional state and how you prepare for the challenges of playing under pressure. He told you not to panic if you are not hitting the ball as well as you can; to review your fundamentals, slow things down and hit baby shots. There is no such thing as the perfect swing, never was, never will be. If you accept the inevitable pressure and concentrate on the process of playing each shot by committing fully to its execution and not the result, you will then and only then have the satisfaction of reaching your potential.'

Timidly, I replied, 'I know you're right, Tail Gunner. I became a good player through determination and spirit. As a kid, I learned to visualize my shots, react to the target and play instinctively. As I got older and learned more about theory, I developed an overactive mind that incessantly critiqued my own performance.'

'That's right! Stop analysing everything and just play the game!'

After that blast of exasperation we played on in silence. I thought I had better be careful what I said next or I might lose my last ghost. Tail Gunner enjoyed the little par 3 pitch-and-putt 14th. Playing only slightly longer than 100 yards from the tee to a shelf green chiselled out of a narrow ledge that over-looks the beach, he expertly guided a 9-iron to within 5 feet of the cup, setting up a 'gimmee' birdie that squared matters between us once again.

Greg Norman claims that the 15th is the first hole he saw when he surveyed the land by helicopter for the first time. No wonder it has turned out to be such a beautiful, natural-looking golf hole, fitting perfectly into its surroundings. From the elevated tee, the fairway deceives one into believing it to be 150 yards away and about 80 yards wide, but a big hit is required to reach the short grass. Tail Gunner and I were both up to the challenge and we made pars. Match still all square.

We were now close to the beach once again and I could see that Tail Gunner was preoccupied and pining to go after Jones and Co. Realizing that we would have all of eternity to play and talk golf soon enough, we said our goodbyes without emotion.

Finishing out the round alone without any further incident did not take very long. As I stood on the intimidating 18th tee, overlooking the beach, I could see that the tide had receded further than usual, leaving a large expanse of sandy beach. About a mile away, underneath the 9th green, I could have sworn that I saw Jones, Ridley, Keeler, Haultain, Mackenzie, Fleming and Tail Gunner hitting balls along the hard sand.

When I reached the clubhouse, Brian Shaw, the Doonbeg head professional, was standing at the door. In his usual friendly manner he greeted me by asking, 'How did you get on?'

'Out of this world – this place is like playing in golf heaven!' I said, with more truth than Brian could ever have realized. 'Where's the Shark? I have a golf ball belonging to him.'

'Greg left by helicopter about half an hour ago. He had to catch a transatlantic flight at Shannon. In all fairness, he told me you were sizzling out there and he wants to play with you again next time he's here.'

'Sure, no problem – but he might be surprised by who turns up to join us.'

ONLY GOLF SPOKEN HERE

Ivan Morris is a 'golf nut'. He lives it, eats it and dreams it. As a low single-digit-handicap golfer for almost fifty years, he has played in amateur and professional championships all over the world. To his great delight, along the way Ivan met with some of golf's best players and most unusual characters. The list includes Tiger Woods, Payne Stewart, Sam Snead, Gary Player, Christy O'Connor Sr, an Irish teammate known as 'Tail Gunner' Carew and an Irish caddie known as 'The Rooney.'

In *Only Golf Spoken Here*, Morris presents an amusing, self-deprecating account of his memories and feelings about a game that continues to tantalize and frustrate him after a lifetime of playing it. His opinions and insights – from a distinctive Irish viewpoint – make highly entertaining and informative reading for anyone with an interest in golf, Ireland or both. Because of his book Morris was voted Golf Nut of the Year in 2001 by the Golf Nut Society of America, the first 'foreign national' to be given this dubious accolade.

Only Golf Spoken Here may be purchased directly from the author: c/o Calamint House, PO Box 3339, Manchester M8 4XX, UK.
Email: imorr@utvinternet.com
Price: €20.00 including p&p.

*Reviews for **Only Golf Spoken Here***

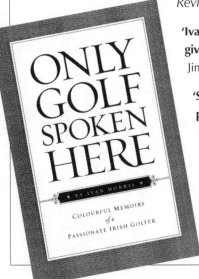

'Ivan Morris has written a book which gives a unique insight into Irish golf'.
Jimmy Woulfe, *Evening Echo*

'Subtitled "colourful memoirs of a passionate Irish golfer", this book is no glossy guide to the "dos" and "dont's" of golf, but a round of insights, incidents, characters and episodes from a golfer's golfer . . . the record of a lifetime and loving every minute of it'.
Dermot Walsh, *Limerick Leader*

THE POCKET GUIDE TO
GOLF COURSES

Playing golf in the 21st century, whether in your own back yard or around the world, there is an increasingly large number of courses to choose from. Each and every course is different. Which will give you a real challenge, and which will give you the most pleasure? And are they as good as they are made out to be? What will you find when you get there? And can you find them at all? This series, at last, is an elegant and concise solution.

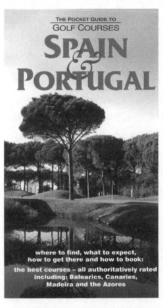

Spain & Portugal

The two most popular tourist golf destinations in Europe.

The best available assessments of the design and facilities at more than 150 courses in Spain and Portugal, including the Balearics, Canaries, Madeira, the Azores and all Costa del Sol, Algarve and Lisbon courses.

240 pages – 270 stunning colour photos

Ireland

The best available assessments of the design and facilities at more than 150 courses in the Republic of Ireland and in Northern Ireland.

240 pages – 300 stunning colour photos

'Finally! A book that tells you the real truth about golf courses! And the pics are terrific.'
John Huggan, *Golf Digest*

'An ideal stocking filler.'
Tim Yeo, *Financial Times*

Beckenham sets new standards in golf course appraisal. The guides list over 150 courses, and combine expert evaluations of courses with assessments of individual holes. They contain full contact details, meticulously researched road directions, ratings of the facilities and a price guide. Also listed are handicap requirements and each course's designer and date of construction. Symbols indicate everything else you need to know. Illustrated throughout with beautiful photographs, generally showing the player's-eye view of the outstanding features and most interesting holes, these visual feasts are mines of accurate and fascinating information.

Beckenham's editorial team, whose number includes leading New Zealand tour professional and course designer Greg Turner, comprises Irish, British and New Zealand golfers (professional and mixed-standard amateurs), all of whom have long been students of golf course design, supported by a panel of widely travelled golfers.

The only series of single-volume, independent, objective and authoritative pocket guides to golf courses.

Excellent for:
- **travelling golfers**
- **residents & holiday-home owners**
- **armchair travellers**
- **golf course design enthusiasts**

For your copies, email look@pocket-golf.com or phone +44 161 702 3339

Indispensable additions to your bag!

Also available from the Pocket Guide team . . .

The GOLF HOUSE

bespoke golf breaks (playing, teaching, and/or design orientated)

The Golf House Marbella, Costa del Sol, Spain (sleeps 4–12, ensuite)
The Golf House Tuscany, Italy (sleeps 4–20, ensuite, in two houses)
The Golf House Cornwall, England (sleeps 4–6)

Self-catering or fully staffed – also for general holidays, weddings, etc.

See www.the-golfhouse.com,
email look@pocket-golf or phone +44 161 702 3339.

PhotoGolf

*Arguably the world's fastest-growing
golf course photo library*

- Ireland 150+ courses
- Spain 100+ courses
- Portugal 50+ courses
- Also Belgium, France, Germany, Italy, UK and USA

We specialize in images from the player's viewpoint for books, magazines, brochures, websites – with satisfied clients worldwide.

Other beautiful angles available, covering most holes on each course.

A new service to the golf industry: subscribe now.
Order retail prints direct – all sizes, framed or unframed:
www.photogolf.ie   www.photogolf.eu   look@pocket-golf.com
Phone +44 161 702 3339

A view from the 1st green at Santo da Serra, Madeira, to the Atlantic.

Beckenham Publishing

Beckenham is an Irish, British and New Zealand owned small independent publisher, whose editorial team includes Greg Turner (shown in action below), the leading New Zealand tour player and course designer. Although a golf and travel specialist, its scheduled list includes quality books on other subjects, especially those where photography is at a premium.

Based in Manchester, England, Beckenham has offices in Spain, Italy and New Zealand. It also owns and manages the PhotoGolf library (*see previous spread*).

Beckenham Publishing Limited, Calamint House, PO Box 3339, Manchester M8 4XX, UK

Tel: +44 161 702 3339   look@pocket-golf.com   www.pocket-golf.com

www.gregturnergolf.com
greg@gregturnergolf.com

A FREE WILL BAPTIST HANDBOOK

HERITAGE, BELIEFS, AND MINISTRIES